D

ELEMENTS OF OPTICS

GENERAL COLLEGE PHYSICS

ELEMENTS OF MECHANICS   by   H. A. ERIKSON
Third Edition, Published 1936

ELEMENTS OF HEAT   by   L. F. MILLER
In preparation

ELEMENTS OF ELECTRICITY   by A. ZELENY
Second Edition, Published 1935

ELEMENTS OF OPTICS   by J. VALASEK
Second Edition, Published 1932

ELEMENTS OF ACOUSTICS   by J. W. BUCHTA
In preparation

Published by the

McGRAW-HILL BOOK COMPANY, INC.

NEW YORK AND LONDON

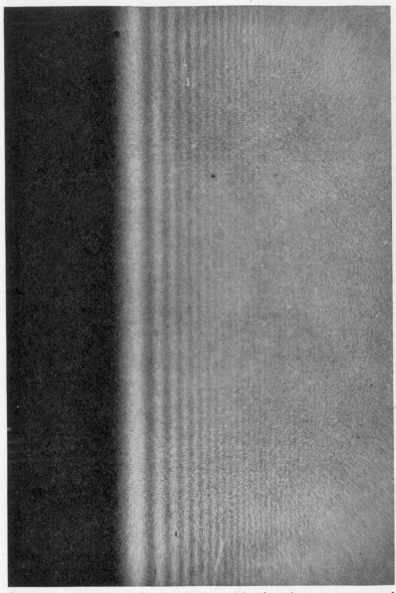

Frontispiece.—The edge of the shadow of a straight edge using a narrow source of light (see Chapter XI).

ELEMENTS OF OPTICS

BY

JOSEPH VALASEK, Ph.D.

Associate Professor of Physics, University of Minnesota

SECOND EDITION
THIRD IMPRESSION

McGRAW-HILL BOOK COMPANY, Inc.

NEW YORK AND LONDON

1932

THE MAPLE PRESS COMPANY, YORK, PA.

Modern civilization rests upon physical science, for it is physical science that makes intelligence and moral energy stronger than brute force.—HUXLEY.

PREFACE

This text is written to fill the need for a modern textbook of optics for a beginning course of college grade extending over three months. Optics is often presented as an appendix to some other branch of physics. Thus, in the various available texts, it is found that usually the section dealing with optics is too brief. In other cases, there is little mention of the many modern developments in this field. Since, at the present time, optics is the center of activity in physical research, no treatment of the subject can be complete if modern spectroscopy, quantum theory, atomic physics, and relativity are neglected. On the other hand, the inclusion of these subjects must not be at the expense of the older and well-established fundamental principles. It is aimed in this text to preserve a proper balance between the old and the new in optics and to lead the student to the realization that this is a subject in which there is constant growth and development through experimental and theoretical research.

The text is for students who have had some physics, covering at least mechanics, and enough mathematics to include the fundamentals of geometry, algebra, and trigonometry.

The second edition is a thorough revision of the text along the lines suggested by four years of classroom experience with the first edition. Many changes have been made to include new developments and new points of view. Numerous problems have been added from the examination papers of recent years. A chapter on the Nature of Light has been written in which the various theories are reviewed and compared. Photographic illustrations of the less easily demonstrated optical phenomena have been produced to supplement the verbal description which by itself is always inadequate.

The author wishes to acknowledge the assistance of Leila M. Valasek, who has read the proofs and has offered many helpful suggestions. The author is also indebted to Professor J. W. Buchta of this University for comments arising from his classroom experience with the first edition. The pinhole photograph is the work of Lawrence Berman, and the spectrograms showing the Zeeman effect were made by Edwin Ebbighausen. To these and to others who have helped produce this book, the author expresses his sincere thanks.

JOSEPH VALASEK.

MINNEAPOLIS, MINN.,
October, 1932.

CONTENTS

CHAPTER IV

THE WAVE THEORY OF LIGHT

CHAPTER V

REFLECTION

CHAPTER VI

REFRACTION

CHAPTER VII

LENSES

CHAPTER VIII

OPTICAL INSTRUMENTS

CHAPTER IX

COLOR

CHAPTER XIV

THE THEORY OF RELATIVITY

CHAPTER XV

THE NATURE OF LIGHT

ELEMENTS OF OPTICS

CHAPTER I

LIGHT AND ITS PROPAGATION

1. Introduction.—Many of our most important sense perceptions and nearly all scientific measurements or observations involve, in some way, our sense of vision. This important place of visual phenomena in our lives makes their study not only interesting but also useful in that new methods of extending and aiding vision are suggested. In fact, the development of optical methods and instruments has led to great progress in many sciences and has even resulted in the creation of new fields of study, as, for example, astrophysics and bacteriology.

The sensation of seeing is produced in some way by the effect of an external agency on the eye. We shall call this agency *visible radiant energy*, or *light*, and shall restrict ourselves chiefly to the study of its properties and uses. The study of light has led to the discovery of new radiations such as ultra-violet rays, which, though invisible to the eye, have important applications. The systematic treatment of radiation phenomena of all kinds comprises the branch of physics known as *optics*. It is one of the oldest of sciences, for the utilization of optical principles in the construction and use of simple instruments, such as lenses and mirrors, dates back to at least 300 B.C.

2. Sources of Light.—The usual sources of light are bodies which radiate light because of their high temperature. About 525°C. is the minimum temperature producing a visible glow in an otherwise dark room. At first the glow is a very dull red, practically gray, but as the temperature is raised it becomes red, orange, then yellow, then white, and finally a dazzling blue-white. The sun, the crater of an arc lamp, and the incandescent lamp all emit light because of high temperature. Their temperatures are, respectively, 6000°C., 4000°C., and 2400°C.

Nitrogen-filled tungsten-filament lamps operate at about 2700°C. The higher the temperature, the greater the efficiency of a thermal radiator. This rule holds only up to 6000°C.; at still higher temperatures the efficiency falls off again. The dependence of efficiency on temperature arises from the fact that a thermal radiator emits both visible and invisible radiations. At 6000°C. the greatest percentage of the energy radiated is visible light. The characteristics of thermal radiators will be taken up in a later chapter.

It is possible to produce light by electrical or chemical excitation without using an especially high temperature. This is popularly referred to as "cold light." The Cooper-Hewitt mercury-vapor lamp is a good example. The firefly, luminous paint, and other phosphorescent substances are other examples of this type of source. Such emission will be discussed later.

3. The Nature of Light.—There has been much speculation as to the nature of light. Some of the old Greek philosophers thought that we saw by the interaction of something emitted by the eye with something coming from the thing perceived. Demokritos and Epikur, however, advanced a theory that light consists of tiny particles shot out by the source. A similar theory was supported by Newton.

The theory accepted at the present time is a modification of the electromagnetic theory, which assumes that light consists of waves of the same type as radio waves but with a much shorter wave length. An electromagnetic wave consists of periodically varying electric forces traveling through the transmitting substances. Such a varying electric disturbance is always accompanied by magnetic forces; hence the wave is called electromagnetic. While the wave length of radio waves is usually 400 meters or more, the wave length of visible light waves lies between 0.00000038 and 0.00000076 meter. For light waves, the atoms themselves are the radio transmitters while the eye is the receiver which is permanently "tuned" to receive only the limited range of wave lengths given above. The electromagnetic theory was proposed by Faraday, a brilliant experimenter of the early nineteenth century, and was developed theoretically by Maxwell long before radio waves were known to exist. When Hertz discovered these waves in 1888, he not only established the electromagnetic theory on a firmer basis but also made possible the invention of wireless telegraphy and telephony. Moreover, the electromagnetic theory has been extremely useful in correlating practically all known facts about light and the optical properties of materials. The idea that light consists of waves is in itself very fruitful. The reason that the wave theory had a serious rival in Newton's corpuscular theory was the idea prevalent in Newton's time that waves could not travel in straight lines and cast sharp shadows as light does. Later this was satisfactorily demonstrated to be due to the short wave length of light waves. Calculations as to the expected bending of light into shadows have been completely verified, since, as will be shown, there is a small but very definite effect.

The subject is not a closed one, however, since recent work has shown the simple theory to be incomplete, for there are a number of phenomena, dealing particularly with exchanges of energy between matter and radiation, which are not easily included in the old electromagnetic theory. No perfectly satisfactory modification has yet been developed. One of the theories developed in recent years is a combination wave and corpuscular theory. This theory and the experiments which support it will be reviewed in Chap. XV. For the present, the most use will be made of the electromagnetic theory, for there is no doubt that light belongs to the family of electromagnetic radiations and that it has many, if not all, of the properties of waves.

4. Rectilinear Propagation.—One of the first properties of light that comes to one's attention is that, in any uniform medium, light travels in straight lines. In fact, this property of light often is used as a criterion for straightness. To test the straightness of a stick, one sights along an edge; even in astronomy, surveying, or in aiming a gun, one makes use of the principle of rectilinear propagation in so far as the medium is uniform. One also observes that the edge of a shadow is always in line with the source and the edge of the obstacle. If the source is small or far away, like a distant arc light, the shadow will be very definitely bounded. If the source is large, this is not so. In this case, there will be a region of partial shadow called the *penumbra* in which there is a transition from full illumination to complete shadow or *umbra*. This effect is readily explained by considering every point on the source as casting its own shadow. The region where all of these shadows overlap receives no light from the source (see Fig. 1). The region outside all of the shadows receives full illumination. Between these there is a uniform gradation. If, instead of casting the shadow on a screen, one looks toward the obstacle and source from the position of the screen, then one sees that when the eye is in the complete shadow the obstacle entirely blocks out the source. In the penumbra there is a "partial eclipse" of the source. The application of this to the explanation of partial and total eclipses of the sun is quite evident.

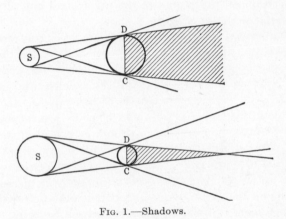

Fig. 1.—Shadows.

If the source is made small, the penumbra narrows down and the shadow is more sharply bounded. If the source is very small, say some fraction of a millimeter in diameter, and if the distances to obstacle and to screen are a meter or so, then, by close observation of the edge of the shadow, it can be seen that it is not perfectly sharp. It is found that the light bends slightly into the geometrical boundaries and that parallel bands of alternate light and darkness line their outside edge. This is illustrated in the frontispiece. The phenomenon is called diffraction and will be studied later. Here we are not particularly concerned with this effect, for if the sources are moderately large and the light passes through no small holes, then, for all practical purposes, light does travel in straight lines.

5. Pinhole Images.—The formation of undistorted images by small openings is a direct consequence of the rectilinear propagation of light. The openings must be small, but large enough to eliminate diffraction effects. For most purposes a moderately sized pinhole will serve. If the lens of a camera is removed and the pinhole substituted, an image of the objects in front of the camera will be cast on the plate. The image, however, will not be very bright, since the pinhole allows little light to pass through it. If the hole is made larger, the image becomes proportionately brighter, but it also becomes less distinct. This image is the result of the incidence on the plate of cones of light radiating from all the points of the object and bounded by the edges of the pinhole. Figure 2 shows three of the cones and

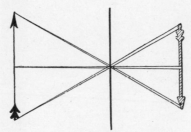

FIG. 2.—Pin-hole image.

their spots on the plate. All such spots fuse to produce the uniform image seen. Since the spots of light all have the color and relative intensity of the point from which they originate, the image is entirely similar to the object. Evidently, if the image is to be sharp, the spots must be small. Up to a certain limit, this can be carried out by using a very small opening; but diffraction, or spreading, and loss of light soon make the image indistinct and dim. A large opening, on the other hand, lets through more light; but the image is diffuse. The use of a lens enables one to obtain both sharpness and brightness of image. This is the advantage of a lens over a pinhole.

On the other hand, pinholes give an image having a pleasing softness which permits artistic effects. Figure 3 is an example of pinhole photography.

6. Rays of Light.—Without giving them a name, we have been tracing the propagation of light by means of lines drawn from the source. These lines which show the direction in which light travels are called *rays*. In a homogeneous medium they are simply straight unbroken lines. When they meet an interface of two media, like air and water, or air and glass, or water and glass, they suddenly change direction and branch off as shown in Fig. 4. The rays that come back into the first medium are said to be reflected, while those that continue with more or less of a change in direction in the second medium are said to be refracted rays. Part of the light is reflected and part refracted

Fig. 3.—A pinhole photograph of the Physics Building, University of Minnesota.

at a boundary. The proportions vary, and sometimes the refracted light is absorbed in a short distance.

7. Reflection.—If a beam of light strikes a smoothly polished surface, some or all of the light is reflected in a definite direction. Such reflection is said to be *regular* to distinguish it from the *diffuse* reflection by rough surfaces, such as paper or plaster. In the case of regular reflection, the reflected ray is in a perfectly definite direction lying in the plane of the incident ray and the normal (*i.e.*, perpendicular) to the surface. This plane is called the *plane of incidence*. The angle between the normal and the incident ray is called the *angle of incidence* while the corresponding angle for the reflected ray is called the *angle of reflection*. The law of reflection may be stated in the following form: The reflected ray lies in the plane of incidence, and the angles of incidence and reflection are equal.

8. Refraction.—Usually, some of the light will penetrate into the second medium and suffer a definite change in direction. This refracted ray likewise lies in the plane of incidence when the materials are not crystals, and sometimes even if they are. For the present, only non-crystalline substances will be dealt with, as they are simpler and by far the most commonly used. For a long time, the exact relation of the angles of refraction r and incidence i (Fig. 4) was a mystery. Up to the fifteenth century, tables of angles of refraction for various angles of incidence were drawn up for all the common pairs of substances. They were all determined by direct experiment. Such studies of refraction were made by Ptolemy (about 140A.D.), by

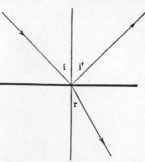

FIG. 4.—Reflection and refraction.

Al Hazen, an Arabian astronomer (about 1000), and by others. No law of refraction was found. As an approximate law for use in the design of telescopes, Kepler in 1611 used the formula

$$\frac{i}{r} = n,$$

where n is a constant depending upon the materials. For glass in air, the value of n is about $\frac{3}{2}$. Kepler stated that this law holds up to angles of 30 degrees, but that depends on the accuracy desired. The smaller the angle, however, the more exact is the formula; for angles of less than 8 degrees, the error is less than 1 per cent. Snell was the first to give the correct law (about 1620), namely,

$$\frac{\operatorname{cosec} r}{\operatorname{cosec} i} = n$$

Descartes, in 1637, first gave the more convenient equivalent of Snell's law as it is usually given nowadays

$$\frac{\sin i}{\sin r} = n.$$

It is evident now why Kepler's formula holds only for small angles. The constant n is different for each pair of substances and is called the *index of refraction* of the second substance with respect to the first. The index of water with respect to air is 1.33; for glasses of various compositions the indices with respect to air lie between 1.4 and 1.9. For ordinary crown glass, it is 1.55. Indices with respect to vacuum are called *absolute* indices and are slightly greater than indices with respect to air, the conversion factor being 1.00029, which is the index of refraction of air itself with respect to a vacuum. This relationship will be derived in the chapter on refraction.

9. Transmission and Absorption.—Accompanying refraction, there is always more or less absorption of light in the refracting material. If there is no change in color, the absorption is said to be *general*, otherwise it is *selective*. The latter type of absorption takes place when some colors in the incident light are absorbed more strongly than others. For any wave length, or color, the fraction by which the intensity is reduced in passing through a small distance dx in the material is the same at all depths. This is written in mathematical form as

$$\frac{dI}{I} = -a\,dx,$$

where dI is the change in the intensity I in the small distance dx, and a is a constant depending on the material and the color of the light. The negative sign is used to indicate that the change in I is a decrease.

The above formula applies only if dx is so small that the corresponding dI is infinitesimal. If this condition is not satisfied, the absorbing material must be subdivided into sufficiently thin layers of thickness dx. The intensity decreases by the same fraction in each of these layers. This leads to an exponential decrease over any appreciable path in the substance. The intensity I of the light after passing through a distance x in the absorbing material is given by

$$I = I_o\, e^{-ax},$$

where I_o is the intensity at the starting point at which $x = 0$, and e is the base of natural logarithms, namely, 2.71828, while a is the *coefficient of absorption.* This coefficient gives the rapidity with which I diminishes, its reciprocal being equal to the distance over which the intensity decreases to $1/e^{th}$ of its original value. The numerical value of a depends on the medium and on the wave length of the light. If a is constant over the visible spectrum, the absorption is said to be general. If a varies with wave length, the relative intensities of the different wave lengths in the original light are changed. This produces color and therefore the absorption is termed selective (Chap. IX). Figure 5 gives the intensity curves for two wave lengths λ_1 and λ_2 for which a is 0.5 and 2.0, respectively. It is seen that, starting with the same intensities,

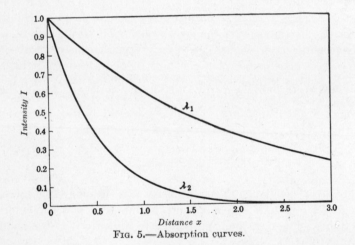

Fig. 5.—Absorption curves.

the relative amount of the two colors changes with thickness of absorbing substance. In fact, a thickness may be found which reduces λ_2 to negligible proportions. An absorber of this thickness could be used as a "color filter" for λ_1. These considerations hold not only for light but also for many other kinds of radiation.

If the refracting material has fine irregularities in its interior or on its surface, the refraction will be *diffuse*, and the material is said to be *translucent* instead of transparent. Diffuse and regular refraction are related in the same way as diffuse and regular reflection.

Problems

1. An image of a man 6 ft. tall is formed by a pinhole camera 10 ft. away. How large is the image on a plate 8 in. from the pinhole? *Ans.* 4.8 in.

2. Prove that, when a mirror is tilted through an angle a, the reflected beam is rotated through an angle equal to $2a$.

3. Light incident at an angle of 50° is refracted by a block of glass having an index of refraction equal to 1.52; what is the direction of the refracted light in the glass? *Ans.* 30° 16′ with the normal.

4. Explain total, partial, and annular eclipses of the sun.

5. Prove that the transmission factor $T = I/I_o$ for an absorber of thickness "x" is equal to the transmission factor for a unit thickness of the absorber raised to the "x" power.

6. A glass 2 mm. thick transmits 50 per cent of the incident light; what will be the transmission factor of a glass 1 mm. thick? *Ans.* 70.7 per cent.

7. A colored glass 1 mm. thick transmits 75 per cent of red light and 50 per cent of blue light; what will be the relative intensity of red to blue after passing through 4 mm. of the glass—the intensities being originally equal? *Ans.* 5.06.

8. Sunlight passes through a rectangular opening and strikes a screen. How does the shape of the patch of light depend on the size of the opening? Explain.

CHAPTER II

PHOTOMETRY

10. Illumination.—The illumination of a surface diminishes when its distance from the source is increased. To make clear the exact manner of variation, some exact definition of *illumination* must be made. By this term will be meant the amount of light energy falling on a unit of area of the surface in a unit of time. The rate of flow of light energy is often called the *light flux*, so that, according to our definition, illumination is light flux per unit area. As may readily be imagined, it is very difficult to measure it in absolute units, *i.e.*, ergs per square centimeter

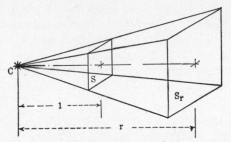

Fig. 6.—Inverse square law.

per second, but, as will be shown below, it is easy to measure it relatively to certain commonly accepted standards. This is done by applying the law for the variation of the illumination I with the distance r of the source from the illuminated surface. This fundamental law of photometry is derived as follows:

Let C (Fig. 6) represent a single source which emits light at a constant rate through the rectangle S at a unit distance from C. The light is propagated in straight lines; hence, after traveling some distance r, it all passes through some rectangle similar to S which shall be designated S_r. The sides of this rectangle are to the corresponding sides of the first as r is to 1. The areas are therefore in the ratio of r^2 to 1. That is,

$$S_r = Sr^2.$$

Now if the medium is nonabsorbing, the light flux L will be the same through both rectangles. Hence, by definition, the illumination of S_r will be

$$I = \frac{L}{S_r} = \frac{L}{Sr^2}.$$

Moreover, the illumination I_o of S will be equal to L/S. Substitution in the above gives

$$I = \frac{I_o}{r^2}.$$

In words, this states that the illumination of a surface by a single source varies inversely as the square of the distance. It is called the *inverse square law*. Usually, I is measured in terms of the illumination which would be given by a standard candle at a unit distance from the surface. This unit of illumination is called the *foot-candle* or the *meter-candle* depending on the units of distance employed. The value of I_o is 1 foot-candle or 1 meter-candle if the source is a unit candle. If it is not a unit candle, the value of I_o tells how many more times as much light energy is radiated by the source to the illuminated surface than if a candle were used. This is called the *candlepower* of the source. Since $I_o = C$, numerically, the inverse square law may be written in the form:

$$I = \frac{C}{r^2}.$$

The practical unit of *light flux* is the *lumen*. One lumen is the rate of flow of energy normally through a unit area at a unit distance from a unit source. Hence a source having a uniform intensity of 1 candlepower in all directions radiates 4π lumens. To determine the light flux to an illuminated surface, one usually employs its relation to illumination:

$$L = IS.$$

The *brightness* of a *surface* is usually expressed in terms of candlepower per square foot. Sometimes brightness is expressed in *lamberts*. One *lambert* is the brightness of a surface which radiates 1 lumen for each square centimeter. Candlepower per square centimeter is equal to $1/\pi$ times the brightness in lamberts.

11. The Cosine Law.—When light does not strike a surface normally, the illumination is reduced. Let θ be the angle of incidence. By definition, the illumination is $I = L/S$. The light flux L which is spread over the inclined surface S would be spread over S' if the area were normal to the rays (Fig. 7). Now $S' = S \cos \theta$; hence

$$I = \frac{L}{S'} \cos \theta = I' \cos \theta.$$

The illumination will also depend on the distance as well as on the angle of incidence. In general, since $I' = I_o/r^2$,

$$I = I_o \frac{\cos \theta}{r^2} = C \frac{\cos \theta}{r^2}.$$

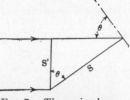

To find the illumination at any point when several sources are present, the illuminations at that point due to each source are added together. Likewise,

FIG. 7.—The cosine law.

if the source is of appreciable size in comparison with the distance r, it must be subdivided into small elements of area. The resultant illumination will not follow the inverse square law exactly.

12. Photometry.—The procedure of comparing intensities of sources is called *photometry*. Essentially, this always consists of using some device for matching the intensities of illumination of some test screen by the two sources to be compared. The illuminations are usually adjusted by varying the distances of the sources from this screen. When equalized, $I_1 = I_2$ for the two sources.
Hence,

$$\frac{C_1}{r_1^2} = \frac{C_2}{r_2^2}$$

or

$$C_1 = C_2 \frac{r_1^2}{r_2^2}.$$

If the intensity of one of the sources is given in candlepower, for instance, then the intensity of the other source can be found in the same units by an application of the above formula. As the formula indicates, the candlepowers are directly proportional to the squares of the distances from the screen.

All methods of photometry do not necessarily employ the inverse square law, for there are other standardizable procedures for equalizing the intensities which are to be compared. In one of these a revolving sector disc is employed, the light passing through it being reduced in average intensity in the same ratio as the angular opening of the sector bears to 2π. The disc is often made in two parts which are mounted so that the opening can be adjusted while the disc is in rotation. Other photometric methods employ calibrated absorbing wedges. Still others use two nicol prisms (Art. 116).

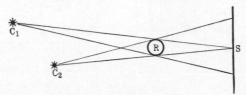

FIG. 8.—Rumford photometer.

13. Rumford Shadow Photometer.—The simplest practical photometer is one devised by Count Rumford. The two sources C_1 and C_2 each cast a shadow of a rod on a screen S (Fig. 8). The positions of the lights are adjusted until the shadows are close together and equally intense. One of the shadows receives light from only C_1 and the other from only C_2. When the shadows are equally dark, the illuminations of the screen by each of the sources are equal and the above formula is immediately applicable.

14. Bunsen Grease-spot Photometer.—Another simple type of photometer employs a test screen which is partially translucent, like paper with a grease spot. This is situated between the two sources. The spot transmits in either direction the same fraction of the light falling on it, and the area around the spot reflects diffusely a definite fraction of the light, so that there is a contrast between the spot and the rest of the screen. The distance of one of the lights from the grease spot is varied until the contrast is equal on both sides. The illuminations are then equal. It is customary to use a mirror on each side of the screen so that both sides can be seen at once. When a match is obtained, $I_1 = I_2$, and the above equations apply.

15. Lummer-Brodhun Photometer.—A more accurate form of photometer is one known as the Lummer-Brodhun. The comparison screens consist of two identical surfaces of white, diffusely reflecting material which are viewed by a set of glass prisms having totally reflecting and transmitting portions. These are so put together that the field is divided into a set of interlacing and sharply bounded areas, illuminated entirely either by one of the sources or by the other. The sharply interlacing field enables one to make accurate settings. Two common

FIG. 9.—Field of Lummer-Brodhun photometer.

forms of field are shown in Fig. 9. The shaded areas are illuminated by one of the sources, while the unshaded areas are illuminated by the other. The conditions for obtaining a match and the equations used in the calculations of the results are the same as before.

16. Flicker Photometer.—There is difficulty in the use of all the above methods if the two sources have even a slight difference in color. In this case better results are obtained either by using a properly tinted screen whose percentage transmission is known and can be corrected for, or by using a flicker photometer. The flicker photometer presents to the eye in rapid succession two surfaces each illuminated by one of the sources. The speed of interchange is made just high enough so that one cannot see the two colors alternately but sees instead an average color mixture. Unless the two sources are of equal intensity, however, the light will seem to flicker. The distances r_1 and r_2 are adjusted so that the flicker disappears and the same formula is applied as in the preceding.

17. Standards of Intensity.—These methods are, all of them, merely comparison methods, so that the intensity of one of the lamps should be known in terms of some conventional units. In practice, the unit of intensity of source is usually taken to be that of a standard candle. Although the standard candle is defined by law to be a candle of spermaceti, six of which weigh

1 pound, which burns at the rate of 120 grains per hour, this standard is too variable to be of much practical use. Much more reliable sources have been in use in various countries: the Harcourt pentane lamp in England, the Hefner amyl-acetate lamp in Germany, and the Carcel colyza oil lamp in France. Their candlepowers are, respectively, 10.0, 0.90, and 9.62, as certified by the International Congress of Weights and Measures.

The best practical standard is a properly constructed and carefully tested incandescent lamp operated always at a constant voltage. When constructed with a large bulb, to avoid blackening, and when properly aged, it is the most reliable working standard. Such a lamp must be calibrated in terms of one of the above standards and checked from time to time. This service is given by the U. S. Bureau of Standards.

18. Practical Illumination.—The illumination of a book for reading should be about 3 foot-candles. As the name implies, this illumination is that produced by a light of 3 candlepower at a distance of 1 foot. It is also equal to the illumination produced by a light of 12 candlepower at 2 feet, or 27 candlepower at 3 feet. These calculations do not take into account the light which is diffusely reflected from the walls and ceiling of the room. This often amounts to two to four times the direct illumination when the walls are light in color, so that actually only one-third or one-fifth of the above candlepower need be used.

Below are some common illuminations:

TABLE I

	Foot-candles		
Full sunlight	2,000.	to	6,000.
For drafting	5.	to	10.
For reading	2.	to	3.
For street lighting	0.1	to	0.6
Full moonlight	0.02	to	0.03

The range of variation is much greater than is usually realized. This is because of the adaptability of the eye to a big range of brightness levels.

Instruments for measuring illuminations are called *illuminometers*. They are photometers in which a surface illuminated by a standard lamp is compared with a similar surface illuminated from outside. One of the best of these is the Macbeth illuminometer. The distance of the standard lamp is adjusted until the two surfaces are equally illuminated. This setting is facilitated by the use of Lummer-Brodhun prisms. The scale on which the distance of the standard lamp is indicated is divided directly in foot-candles so that no calculation is required. A second standard lamp is supplied to be used in calibrating the working standard from time to time and thus guard against errors due to deterioration of the lamp. The lamps are operated by a battery with an ammeter and rheostat in series, so that one is independent of the condition of the battery.

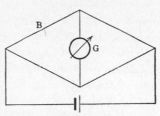

FIG. 10.—Bolometer circuit.

19. Physical Photometry.—One may measure the value of the energy flow in terms of ergs per second, watts, or calories per second by the use of a physical photometer such as the bolometer. This consists of a very thin strip of platinum which is covered with lampblack to absorb all the light (*B*, Fig. 10). Owing to the rise in temperature, the resistance of the strip changes, and this causes a deflection of the sensitive galvanometer

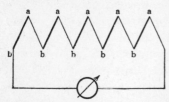

FIG. 11.—Thermopile circuit.

G connected in a "Wheatstone bridge" circuit as shown in Fig. 10. To obtain absolute values of the light energy, one must compare the heating produced by the light to that produced in some measurable way. For example, one may have the light fall on a very thin strip of metal very close to the bolometer filament. The latter is heated indirectly by the radiation from this strip. After observing the resulting deflection, one may pass an electric current through the strip of metal of a magnitude such as to duplicate the deflection produced by the absorbed light. The rate at which electrical energy must be supplied is the product of the current and the voltage drop along the strip. This equals the light flux in watts which, when multiplied by 10^7, gives the result in ergs per second.

Another device that may be used in the same way is the thermo-pile. This consists of many junctions of dissimilar metals connected in series as shown in Fig. 11. The pairs of metals most frequently used are copper and constantan or bismuth and silver. Any difference in temperature between the junctions at a and the junctions at b causes a current to flow through the galvanometer. The illuminated set of junctions usually have some very small, thin, blackened silver plates soldered to them, while the other set of junctions is protected from the radiation.

These physical photometric methods apply equally well to wave lengths outside of the visible range. They are especially useful in the study of the longer waves (Chap. XIII).

Ordinary sources do not emit much ultra-violet radiation, so that it is not easy to get a bolometer or thermopile which is sensitive enough to be satisfactory in this region of the spectrum. Hence it is preferable to use a photoelectric cell. This consists of a two-electrode vacuum tube (Art. 142) through which a current can pass only when the negative electrode is illuminated. The value of the current is proportional to the light flux. However, these cells have the same failing as the eye—their sensitivity depends very greatly on the wave length. Hence one cannot conveniently use them to compare lights of different color.

The "copper oxide sandwich cell," or "photronic cell," is a newly developed form of photoelectric cell consisting of a copper oxide layer between two electrodes, the forward one being partly transparent. The photoelectrons are shot into the copper oxide layer, causing a difference in potential between the electrodes. A galvanometer connected to the cell gives deflections which are proportional to the illumination intensities.

It is particularly advantageous to use the photographic plate in the photometry of ultra-violet light of low intensity. For each wave length, the photographic plate has a different calibration curve similar to the one shown in Fig. 12. The blackening of the plate is expressed by means of the *density* which is the common logarithm of the ratio of the light transmitted by the clear part of the plate to the intensity transmitted by the blackened part. The abscissas are the common logarithms of the illumination, the time of exposure being kept constant. When photographic plates are used in photometry, great care must be taken to control the exposure, the temperature and time of development, and the composition of the developer. It is best to virtually calibrate each plate by taking test exposures on it, using standardized absorbing screens with a standard source and then comparing densities.

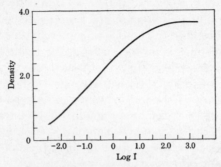

FIG. 12.—Characteristic curve of a photographic plate.

Problems

1. Two lights 1 m. apart are, respectively, of 15 and 25 cp. At what point between them should a screen be placed in order to be equally illuminated by each? *Ans.* 56.3 cm. from brighter.

2. An illumination of about 3 foot-candles is required for reading. What candlepower lamp should be placed in a socket 6 ft. away if three times as much light comes from the walls as from the source directly? *Ans.* 27 cp.

3. A lamp produces a certain illumination on a screen 75 cm. away. On placing a sheet of glass between the lamp and the screen, the lamp must be moved 5 cm. closer to give the same illumination as before. What percentage of the light is transmitted by the glass? *Ans.* 87.1 per cent.

4. If the intensity of illumination produced on a screen 3 m. away from an incandescent lamp is equivalent to that of a Hefner standard (0.90 cp.) at a distance of 50 cm., what is the candlepower of the lamp? *Ans.* 32.4 cp.

5. Three lamps illuminate a surface. Their respective candlepowers are 10, 20, and 30; their respective distances are 6, 10, and 15 ft.; and the respective angles of incidence of the light on the surface are 60, 45, and 30°. What is the illumination? *Ans.* 0.396 foot-candle.

6. Define the following: (*a*) unit of illumination, (*b*) candlepower, (*c*) lumen, (*d*) lambert.

CHAPTER III

VELOCITY OF LIGHT

20. The Velocity of Light.—Previous to 1600 the velocity of light was supposed to be infinite. Galileo was the first to question this idea and to try to measure its velocity. He used a method like the one that had been used to measure the velocity of sound. Two observers, first stationed close together and then about a mile apart, exchanged signals by flashing lights. One of the observers noted how long it took for the signals to be relayed back and forth. The difference between the times for the two distances eliminated the times of response of the observers and gave solely the time taken for the light to travel out and then back again. This difference, when averaged over a large number of trials, gave zero for the time of travel but the errors were large enough to still give room for doubt of an infinite velocity for light.

21. Roemer's Method.—In 1675, Roemer, a Danish astronomer, succeeded in finding the velocity by means of observations of the times at which one of Jupiter's satellites was eclipsed by the planet. He found that the times between successive eclipses varied between a maximum of 42 hours, 28 minutes, 56 seconds, when the earth was receding from Jupiter, and 42 hours, 28 minutes, 28 seconds, when the earth was approaching most rapidly. This is evidently due to the fact that the earth, in the first case, moves farther away between two successive eclipses and causes the light to arrive a little later than if the earth were standing still, while, in the second case, the earth moves up to intercept the signal before it would normally reach it. The relative positions of the earth and Jupiter during observations of eclipses during successive "oppositions" and "conjunctions" are shown in the figure (Fig. 13). Since Jupiter rotates once around its orbit in 11.86 years, these positions come about 0.6 year apart. As it takes only a few days for the satellites to revolve around Jupiter, observations on several eclipses can be made before the earth and Jupiter move sensibly from the positions E_1 and J_1, for example. If these observations are used to predict the times of the following eclipses, the predicted times will be found too early by a greater and greater amount until the earth and Jupiter are in the positions E_2 and J_2, when the predicted times will be too early by about 1,000 seconds. After this the eclipses will occur closer and closer to the scheduled times

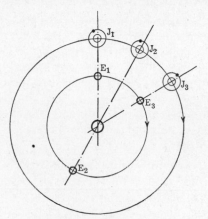

Fig. 13.—Roemer's method.

until when the earth and Jupiter are in the positions E_3 and J_3, they will again occur according to prediction. Roemer decided that the 1,000 seconds maximum discrepancy was due to the fact that it took just that long for the light to travel the distance by which E_2J_2 is greater than E_1J_1. This distance is equal to the diameter of the earth's orbit, which is known from astronomical measurements to be 186,000,000 miles. Hence, the velocity of light is

$$\frac{186,000,000}{1,000} = 186,000 \text{ miles per second}$$

or 2.99×10^{10} centimeters per second.

22. Bradley's Method.—In 1727, this result was verified by another astronomer named Bradley, using an entirely different method. He noticed that the stars overhead appeared to move in small orbits with a period of 1 year, even when that part of

their motion due to parallax was accounted for. This newly discovered component of the star's apparent motion was in the same
direction as the motion of the earth in its orbit.   He accounted

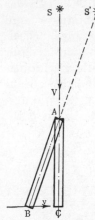

for it by assuming an effect of the velocity of
the earth on the apparent direction of propagation of light, similar to that of a moving car
on the apparent direction of falling rain.   The
observing telescope must be, accordingly,
pointed a little forward to line up with the
apparent direction of propagation of the light
from the star. If S in Fig. 14 represents a
star, and AC a telescope when stationary,
we see that light will travel from S through
A to C if the tube is vertical and pointing at
the star. If, however, the telescope is moving
with a velocity v, the light which enters at
the center of A will not line up with the center
of C and may even strike the side.   The

Fig. 14.—Bradley's
method.

amount of tilt necessary to prevent this is
such that the time t taken for the light to travel from A to C,
which is equal to AC/V, is the same as the time taken by B
to move over to C, which is equal to BC/v.
Hence

$$\frac{BC}{v} = \frac{AC}{V}$$

or

$$\frac{v}{V} = \frac{BC}{AC} = \tan BAC.$$

Measurements give $BAC = 20.45$ seconds and $v = 30,557$ meters
per second, so that

$$V = 3.047 \times 10^{10} \text{ centimeters per second.}$$

23. Fizeau's Method.—In 1849, a French scientist named
Fizeau first used terrestrial sources for measuring the velocity
of light.   Essentially, his method was one for measuring the
extremely short time of transmission by computation from the
angle through which a rapidly revolving disc had turned in
the same time.   It might be said that he invented a "stop watch"

capable of measuring down to 1/100,000 second or better. The arrangement shows considerable ingenuity and is outlined in Fig. 15.

A lens L_1 and an inclined glass plate M_1 cause the light from S to be focused at T, the rim of a disc which contains a large number of slots or teeth around its periphery, like a gear wheel. If the disc D is rotated, the teeth will alternately transmit and cut off the light and cause flashes of light to be sent out through the lens L_2. This lens sends a parallel or "searchlight" beam to the lens L_3 and then to the mirror M_2, which is curved and placed so as to return the light along exactly the same path.

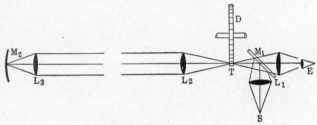

Fɪɢ. 15.—Fizeau's method.

Some of the returning light is transmitted by the glass M_1 and is perceived by the eye at E. If the speed of the disc is only moderate, the eye will perceive a continuous brightness, since the flashes get back so quickly that they will return through the same gap before it moves appreciably. As the speed is increased, there comes a time when a tooth has moved over so as to block the path for the returning beam. The eye then observes no light. If the speed is doubled, the light will reappear through the gap next to the one it originally passed through. If the speed is tripled, the light will disappear again, and so on. The time taken for the light to travel the distance $2TM_2$ is equal to the time taken for the wheel to turn through some measurable angle. This angle is that of one tooth when the speed is such that the transmission by the next gap is observed. The velocity of the disc necessary to cause this to occur is measured and the time for the disc to rotate through any angle is then easily calculated. The distance $2TM_2$ divided by the time taken by the disc to rotate through an angle of one tooth, in case the first transmission is used, gives the velocity of light. Fizeau used a wheel having 720 teeth and had the light travel 8.633 kilometers and back. He found that at every increase in the speed of rotation by 24.2 revolutions per second the light came through to the eye. The latest value obtained by this method is 3.004×10^{10} centimeters per second, agreeing with the astronomical results within experimental error.

24. Foucault's Method.—The best method yet devised is that of Foucault as improved by Michelson and Newcomb. In this a rotating mirror M_1 reflects light from S (Fig. 16). The light is made to travel in a parallel beam by the lens L to a distant mirror M_2 which causes it to retrace its path. If the mirror M_1 is set in

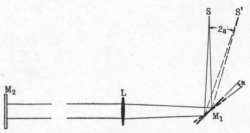

Fig. 16.—Michelson's method.

rapid rotation the light will come back from M_2 after M_1 has turned through some definite angle a and an image of S will be formed at another point S'. An application of the law of reflection shows that if the mirror turns through an angle a the angles of incidence and reflection both will be changed by the amount of a and the reflected beam will therefore move through an angle $2a$. The angle is usually a small one and in radians can be written as equal to SS'/SM_1 or $d/r = 2a$. The time T taken for the mirror to turn through an angle a is $a/2\pi$ times the time for one revolution. If the number of revolutions per second is n, then this time is

$$T = \frac{a}{2\pi n} \text{ seconds.}$$

In this interval the light travels the distance $2M_1M_2 = 2L$. The velocity of light V is then given by

$$V = \frac{2L}{T} = \frac{4\pi nL}{a} = \frac{8\pi nLr}{d}.$$

For example, Michelson's data were

$L = 625$ meters,
$n = 257$ revolutions per second,
$r = 9$ meters,
$d = 133$ millimeters.

These give a value for V of 2.998×10^{10} centimeters per second.

The accurate measurement of the velocity of light is not only desirable because it is a fundamental physical constant, but also because of its possible application in the surveying of large areas by measuring the time to travel from one point to another. For these reasons, Michelson has recently (1924–1931) repeated his measurements with the greatest accuracy so far obtainable. The rotating mirror in these experiments had 8, 12, or 16 sides. Its speed of rotation was adjusted so that the mirror would revolve through, respectively, one-eighth, one-twelfth, or one-sixteenth of a revolution in the time that the light traveled the distance $2L$. The returning beam of light was undeflected when exactly the right speed was obtained.[1] In this modification of the rotating-mirror method, the angle of rotation is predetermined, and only the rate of rotation of the mirror must be measured. This is done by illuminating an edge of a standard tuning fork by the intermittent flashes of light from the rotating mirror. If the frequencies of the fork and of the flashes are equal, the edge of the fork will appear stationary. A slight difference in frequency gives a slowly wandering image of the fork from which one can determine the exact frequency. The light path used was from Mount Wilson to Mount San Antonio, a distance of 35.4 kilometers, which was measured with the greatest possible accuracy by the U. S. Coast and Geodetic Survey. The weighted mean of 1,763 observations on the velocity of light gives the value

$$V = 299,796 \pm 1 \text{ kilometers per second}$$

or

$$V = 186,284 \text{ miles per second.}$$

25. Velocity of Light in Different Media.—Michelson has also measured the velocity of light in water and in carbon disulphide

[1] For details see "Studies in Optics" by Michelson, University of Chicago Press, 1927.

by putting a long tank of the liquid between M_1 and M_2. He showed in this way that light traveled more slowly in these media than in free space.   The ratios of the velocity in air to the velocities in these two media are, respectively, 1.33 and 1.63, being equal to the refractive indices.   The results are of importance and will be referred to again later.

In free space the velocity of light is independent of the color. Star eclipses always show a simultaneous change in intensity of all colors instead of some colors appearing to be cut off sooner. In air and in other gases there is likewise no appreciable difference in the velocity of variously colored lights.   In liquids and solids, however, the velocity is *always* more or less dependent on the color.   For example, Michelson found that red light traveled 1.4 per cent faster than blue in CS_2.   In some media the effects are still more marked.

CHAPTER IV

THE WAVE THEORY OF LIGHT

26. Nature of Light.—The properties of light considered above give some definite clues as to the nature of light. In the first place, it is known that light is a form of energy because it can be converted into other forms of energy, such as electrical, mechanical, heat, and chemical energy. Because of the conservation principle, its arrival at the eye some distance away, at a time later than its disappearance at the source, leads to the conclusion that it exists in some form at intermediate points and at intermediate times. Now, light travels through space with a large but measurable velocity of 3×10^{10} centimeters per second, and we are aware of the transmission of energy with some definite velocity only as associated with matter in motion or with waves traveling through some medium. Accordingly, it seems as though, light must consist either of waves propagated through some all-pervading medium, or it must consist of particles or corpuscles which are of a very penetrating kind in transparent materials. The medium necessary for the first theory, called the *ether-wave theory,* must permeate everything and must exist everywhere, even in the most perfect of vacua. Such a medium is also needed to explain the electrical forces at distances from electrical charges; so it is no entirely new idea peculiar to optical theory.

Before the time of Thomas Young, *i.e.*, before 1800, the corpuscular theory was generally accepted. This preference was largely due to its advocacy by the famous Isaac Newton. As time went on, more and more facts were discovered in contradiction to the corpuscular theory and in harmony with the wave theory as developed by Christian Huyghens, Thomas Young, and Augustin Jean Fresnel, until it was plainly evident that the older theory had to be discarded in favor of the new.

Later the wave theory took on a particular form because of the advances in electromagnetism by Faraday, Maxwell, and Hertz.

The theory most readily applied to the totality of optical facts is that light consists of electromagnetic waves having a very short wave length. However, there are many questions not yet cleared up, some of which are explainable only with the aid of unsatisfactory additional hypotheses. For example, the exact processes by which atoms radiate and absorb light are still but slightly understood. It is known that matter is composed of positive electricity (protons) and negative electricity (electrons) and that the latter may be in distributions or "states" having different energy. During absorption the electrons gain energy from the radiation and pass to a different state, while during emission the reverse transition takes place. It is interesting and very significant that these exchanges of energy between electrons and radiation take place in units of definite amounts of energy called quanta (Art. 135). This is not easy to reconcile with the idea of continuous waves. Many working rules have been discovered which govern these interchanges but the details of the processes are just beginning to be understood.

It is significant that some recent experiments (Art. 146) can best be explained by assuming that light has corpuscular characteristics. Nevertheless, it is essential to think of these corpuscles as guided by accompanying waves in order to not contradict a vast body of experimental fact on the propagation of light.

27. Propagation of Light.—Evidently the strong point of the corpuscular theory was its explanation of the rectilinear propagation of light. On the other hand, the only argument Newton advanced against the wave theory was that waves would bend around obstacles and into shadows like sound. However, further consideration should have suggested that shorter waves cast sharper shadows even in the case of sound, and that the wave length of light is probably small enough so that the sharpness of its shadows can be accounted for by the wave theory. Experiment shows, indeed, that light does bend a little into its shadows and in this respect the wave theory is better able to meet the facts. Consider the photograph of the shadow of an edge in the frontispiece.

The laws of reflection are explained equally well by either theory but in regard to the laws of refraction there is a disagreement, not in the laws themselves but in certain deductions as to velocity, which follow from their explanation. For example, in the case of refraction of light into water from air, the beam is bent toward the normal in the water. The corpuscular theory explains this as due to an attraction of the water for the light corpuscles. Consequently, they must travel faster in the water than in air. In fact, the velocity should be 33 per cent faster in water than in air to give the correct index of refraction. As will be shown very shortly (Art. 44), the wave theory explains the same phenomenon as due to the smaller velocity of light in water than in air, the velocity being 33 per cent *faster in air*. Here is a crucial difference between the two theories which can be settled by measuring the velocity of light in water. This was done by Michelson, who found that light travels less rapidly in water than in air by the exact amount predicted by the wave theory.

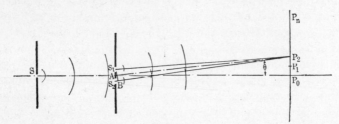

FIG. 17.—Young's experiment.

28. Interference.—In 1800, Thomas Young performed an experiment which showed that light from two similar sources may interfere and cause dark bands to appear at certain places. These experiments led him to uphold the wave theory and to start the series of investigations which finally led to its acceptance in spite of Newton's great prestige.

He found that if light from a narrow source, such as an illuminated slit or a hot wire S (Fig. 17), passes through two narrow scratches S_1 and S_2 through an opaque plate placed parallel to the source and at some distance away, bands of alternating light and darkness appear on a screen at some distance behind the double slit or in an eye placed just behind it. The second method for observing the interference effects shows them brighter but is not so suitable for making measurements. The wave theory explains these light and dark bands as follows: The light effect at any point on the screen is due to the sum of two waves from S_1 and S_2, respectively. Since light is a wave motion, there will be points on the screen whose distances from S_1 and S_2 will differ by just the right amount to cause the wave from S_1 to oppose the wave from S_2 and annul it at these points. At other points the waves will arrive in the same "phase" and double the motion. Thus, for example, P_0, which is equally distant from S_1 and S_2, will get the impulses from both sources always in the same direction, and they will add up at all times to give the double effect, thus causing P_0 to be bright. Near it is a point P_1 which is a half wave ($\frac{1}{2}\lambda$) farther from S_2 than from S_1 where the effects will at all times be equal and opposite. Here there will be darkness. At P_2, with just one wave difference in path, there will be brightness, and so on. In general, whenever the path difference $S_2P_n - S_1P_n$ is an even number of half waves there is brightness at P_n while if it is an odd number of half waves there is darkness at this point. Let the angle P_2AP_0 be called θ and the wave length be called λ. Draw from S_1 a perpendicular to AP_2. The angle it makes with S_1S_2 is equal to θ, and since $S_1P_2 = BP_2$, we have $S_2B = S_2P_2 - S_1P_2$ which is equal to λ because P_2 is the location of the first maximum from the center. Therefore $\lambda = S_2B$. The triangle S_1S_2B is practically a right triangle because of the construction of the side S_1B. This side, although drawn perpendicular to AP_2, is very nearly perpendicular to S_2P_2, because, in Young's experiment, the distance between the two slits is always much smaller than the distance to the screen on which the interference is observed. Therefore $S_2B = a \sin \theta$, where a is the distance S_1S_2. Hence it follows that:

$$\lambda = a \sin \theta.$$

The above gives a method for measuring the wave length of light by measuring the quantities a and $\sin \theta$. The distance a can be measured by means of a micrometer microscope, and θ can be measured by observing the spacing of the dark or bright bands, e.g., P_0P_2. Since θ is very small in any such experiment, we may put $P_2A = P_0A = D$ for all practical purposes, and if we replace P_0P_2 by p, then

$$\sin \theta = \frac{p}{D}$$

which, with the above, gives:

$$\lambda = \frac{ap}{D}.$$

All the quantities on the right can be easily measured.

It is found that λ depends upon the color of the light in any particular medium. For red light in air it is about 0.000065 centimeter and for violet it is 0.000040 centimeter. This explains why the bands have colored edges if a mixture of different wave lengths, such as white light, is used. In such a case, the bands

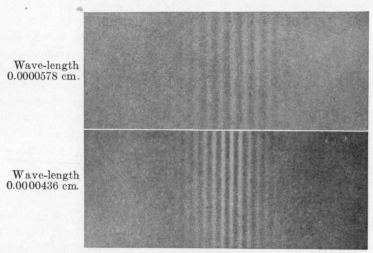

Wave-length
0.0000578 cm.

Wave-length
0.0000436 cm.

FIG. 18.—Young's interference fringes.

come at different places according to the wave length, and hence do not quite superpose. Figure 18 shows the interference bands for two different wave lengths.

If we let ν be the frequency or the number of waves per second, then the number of waves emitted in a second times the length of one wave gives the distance traveled by the first wave in one second. This is V, the velocity of the light, so that we have

$$\lambda\nu = V \text{ or } \nu = \frac{V}{\lambda}.$$

It is found that the wave length of light of any one color is not the same in different materials. For example, the wave length of any color is three-quarters as great in water as it is in air. Since the velocity is also less in the same proportion, the above equation shows that the frequency is unchanged. If the wave length of some color is specified without giving the medium, it will be understood that the wave length given is the value in vacuo. This is very nearly the same as the value in air.

Sometimes the wave number N, which is defined as the number of waves per centimeter, is used instead of frequency. According to this definition

$$N = \frac{1}{\lambda} = \frac{\nu}{V}.$$

Hence wave number and frequency are proportional.

29. Huyghens' Principle.—A very useful principle applying to propagation of waves was first given by Christian Huyghens in a book on optics printed in 1690. He stated that a wave is propagated as though every point on a wave front served as a source for a secondary spherical wavelet which traveled forward only, and that the enveloping surface (tangent) of all the wavelets gives the position of the wave at a later time. Figure 19 shows

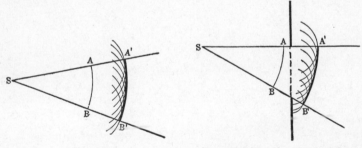

FIG. 19.   FIG. 20.—Huyghens' principle.

a source at S and a wave front at AB at some initial instant. A *wave front* is any surface of equal phase. To find the position of the same wave front at a later time t a set of wavelets with radii Vt is constructed with points on AB as centers. The envelope $A'B'$ gives the position of the wave at the time t.

Another application of the principle is shown in Fig. 20, which shows a wave traveling through an opening. In this case, the centers of the wavelets are taken in the plane of the opening, the radii being equal to V times the time t *less* the time taken to travel to the opening.

Of course, in these two cases the result is so obvious that the application of the principle seems unnecessary. This is why these cases have been chosen as first illustrations. The value of Huyghens' principle will be realized from its application to the less obvious cases of reflection and refraction of light waves to be considered in the following chapters.

CHAPTER V

REFLECTION

30. Reflection by a Plane Mirror.—By applying Huyghens' principle, one may readily find the change in the propagation of a light wave when it is reflected by a plane surface. Let MN (Fig. 21) represent the reflecting surface and let S represent the source of light at a distance u from MN. At a time which is taken as the initial instant, a wave front will be in the position CDE. If the mirror were temporarily removed, it would arrive at $C'D'E'$ at a time t later. With the mirror in place, however, it

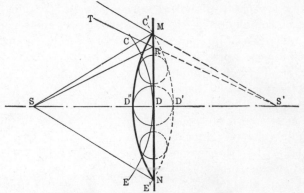

Fig. 21.—Reflection at a plane mirror.

travels backward as soon as it touches the mirror and after the time t it has just been wholly reflected. To find the reflected wave, wavelets are drawn with their centers on the mirror surface. The radii of these wavelets may be found from the fact that if the mirror were removed they would all be tangent to the arc $C'D'E'$ whose center is at S. With the mirror in place, the wavelets have the same radii, but they travel in the opposite direction. Their envelope will be $C'D''E'$, which is the reflected wave. It is similar to $C'D'E'$, and its center S' is the same dis-

34

tance as S from the mirror along the normal SD but is on the other side of the mirror. The point S' will be the center of all reflected rays since in any non-crystalline medium the rays are perpendicular to the wave front and, therefore, if the wave is spherical, they all meet at its center. If SR is any incident ray, the reflected ray will be on a line through R which, extended backward, passes through S'. If the angle of incidence is i it is easy to show geometrically that the angle of reflection is also equal to i.

31. Foci.—Any point toward which or from which a set of rays is directed is called a *focus*. If the rays through one focus also pass through another, the two foci are said to be *conjugate*. The foci S and S' in the above are conjugate foci. The focus S is said to be a *real* focus because the rays actually pass through S, while S' is said to be a *virtual* focus because only the projections of the rays pass through it.

32. Vision.—Of the rays coming from a focus S, a narrow cone will enter the pupil of the eye turned toward it. This cone is focused on some point of the retina and excites the sensation of vision. The sensation is intuitively referred to the point S from which the rays apparently come. Similarly, if a cone of rays from a virtual focus like S' strikes the eye the sensation is referred to the point from which they appear to diverge. To the eye a virtual focus as S' is just as efficient in producing an image on the retina as an equally bright real focus S at the same place.

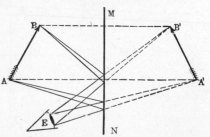

Fig. 22.—Image in a plane mirror.

33. Images.—Suppose an extended object, such as the arrow AB (Fig. 22), is placed in front of a mirror MN. Each point of this object sends out rays of light in a manner similar to S in Fig. 21. Its conjugate focus is therefore at the same distance behind the mirror and is virtual. The conjugate foci of all points on AB will form an image $A'B'$ similar to AB and situated behind the mirror as shown. Cones of rays from AB will appear to come to the eye from $A'B'$. These rays coming from different points are focused on different parts of the retina and cause the image

$A'B'$ to be seen. If the mirror were perfect, it would be invisible, and only the images of objects located in front of it would be seen.

34. Multiple Reflections.—If S be placed between two mirrors A and B which are at an angle with each other, an eye at E will see a set of images. Three of them are shown in the figure (Fig. 23). The cone of rays shown suffers three reflections before entering the eye. More reflections are possible under different conditions. It will be noticed that the image on the retina would be the same if the rays had come from S_A with only two reflections or from S_{AB} with one reflection or from S_{ABA} with no reflection. The triple reflection illustrated in the figure will produce only one

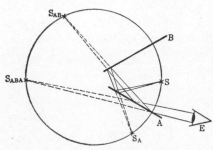

image on the retina and cause the single image S_{ABA} to be seen at the place from which the rays appear to come at the moment they reach the eye. A double reflection first off A and then off B (not shown) will send light rays to the eye in a different direction and cause the image

FIG. 23.—Multiple reflection.

at S_{AB} to be seen. In case of a single reflection off A the light will appear to come from S_A. There are still other possible paths from S to the eye. It is thus evident that a number of images will be seen, each of which corresponds to one of the possible paths the light may follow in coming from S to the eye. The number of possible reflections before the eye is reached increases as the angle between the two mirrors is made smaller. If the mirrors are nearly parallel, a very large number of images, one behind the other, can be seen, the number being limited by the reflecting power of the mirrors.

35. Curved Surfaces.—When a wave is reflected from a curved surface, its curvature is changed unless it happens to be the same as that of the surface. If the incident wave and the surface are both spherical, the reflected wave is very nearly spherical. This statement holds only when the size of the mirror is not large compared to its radius. This is verified experimentally by showing that a sharp point image of any point source is obtained under these conditions. In such a case there is also a definite clear image of any extended object, for this can be treated as an assemblage of points each giving its own distinct image. The position of this image depends on the curvature of the mirror and on the position of the object. The exact relation can be deduced by an application of Huyghens' principle and the use of a simple relation between the radius, R, and sagitta, x (Fig. 24), of an arc of a circle. Let DC be the arc whose center is at A, and whose semichord is y.

In the right triangle ABC, we have

$$R^2 = y^2 + (R^2 - 2Rx + x^2)$$

or

$$x = \frac{y^2}{2R - x} = \frac{y^2}{R(1 + \cos\theta)}$$

which reduces to

$$x = \frac{y^2}{2R},$$

if θ is very small. This last expression is in error by less

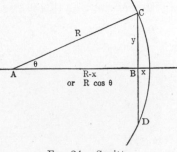

FIG. 24.—Sagitta.

than 1 per cent if θ is less than 11 degrees, since $1 + \cos 11° = 1.98$. The smaller this angle is, the smaller will the error be, as can be easily verified by inspecting a table of trigonometric functions.

36. Concave Mirror.—Consider a concave mirror of radius R, and semichord y, the center being at O (Fig. 25). Let there be a point source or focus at S and let u be the radius of a spherical wave from S just touching the mirror at M and N. This radius is also the distance of the object from the mirror. Applying Huyghens' principle to the problem of finding the reflected wave at the instant that it touches the mirror at B, draw the position of the wave $N''BM''$, considering the mirror to be temporarily removed. The wavelets used to construct the reflected wave are then tangent to $N''BM''$, their centers being on MBN. Their envelope $N'BM'$ is the reflected wave. This wave is nearly spherical if α, β, and γ are small, as was explained before. In fact, this can also be shown by this construction. Since a wave travels in a direction perpendicular to itself, a spherical wave such as this will converge toward its center at S'. This point S' is then the image of S, in other words, S and S' are conjugate foci.

The point S' is in this case a real focus, for the rays actually pass through it. Denote the radius of $M'BN'$ by v which can be taken as the experimentally measured distance of the image from the mirror. To find its relationship to u and R, draw ME and NF parallel to SB and then draw EDF. If the angles designated in the figure are less than 8 degrees, as they should be to get a good image, then $MM' = ME$ to within 1 per cent. Now $MM' = AB$ by construction according to Huyghens' principle so that

$$ME = CD = AB$$

In terms of sagittas this is equivalent to saying that

$$DB - CB = CB - CA$$

or, by transposing,

$$CA + DB = 2CB.$$

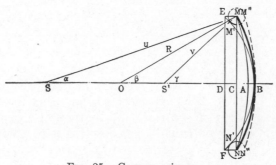

FIG. 25.—Concave mirror.

Applying to this the formula giving sagittas in terms of radii and semichords, this reduces to

$$\frac{y^2}{2u} + \frac{y^2}{2v} = \frac{2y^2}{2R}$$

or

$$\frac{1}{u} + \frac{1}{v} = \frac{2}{R}.$$

If u becomes very large, that is, if the source is moved very far from the mirror, the fraction $1/u$ in the above becomes very small so that if the source is far enough away it can be disregarded in comparison with $1/v$. In this case $1/v = 2/R$, showing that the image approaches a point just half the radius of curvature of the mirror away from it. This point is called the *principal focus* and the distance $R/2$ is called the *focal length* of the mirror. Denoting this quantity by f, we can write

$$\frac{1}{u} + \frac{1}{v} = \frac{1}{f}.$$

When this formula is examined for positions of image for various positions of object, *i.e.*, for various values of u, it is found that v takes on the values indicated in the following table:

	Values of u	Values of v
1	∞	f
2	∞ to R	f to R
3	R	R
4	R to $R/2$	R to $+\infty$
5	$R/2$	$\pm \infty$
6	$R/2$ to 0	$-\infty$ to 0 (negative)

The sixth case in which the object is nearer to the mirror than its principal focus gives negative values of v. The meaning of this is that the reflected wave is curved in the opposite sense to that shown in Fig. 25. The reflected light therefore diverges from a point behind the mirror as in the case of a plane mirror and thus the image is virtual. This result may be easily verified by applying Huyghens' construction to the case of an object closer than the principal focus.

In applications of the mirror formula the signs must always be carefully considered to avoid error in the calculations, and the convention used in this derivation should be followed, namely, that u, v and R should be regarded as positive when on the same side of the mirror, as in the case of a concave mirror giving a real image (Fig. 25); any one of them is to be taken as negative if it is on the other side of the mirror. Thus, if the mirror is convex instead of concave, the formula just derived may be used if the value of R is substituted with a negative sign. This is the only change needed. After calculating v in the ordinary way, its sign tells whether the image is real or virtual. If the sign comes out negative, the image is virtual. To show that the convex-mirror formula is identical with that for the concave mirror if the above rule of signs is adhered to, it will be derived in the following paragraph.

37. Convex Mirror.—Using the same notation and the same general procedure as in the case of the concave mirror, it is found that (Fig. 26)

$$DC = EM = AB$$

In terms of sagittas this gives:

$$AD + AC = BC - AC$$

or

$$AD - BC = -2AC$$

Using the formula for sagittas in terms of radii of curvature, and noting that v and R are negative according to the rule of signs

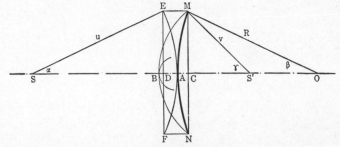

FIG. 26.—Convex mirror.

it has been decided to use (compare Figs. **25** and **26** in this respect), the following values are substituted above:

$$AD = \frac{y^2}{2u}; BC = \frac{y^2}{-2v}; \text{ and } AC = \frac{y^2}{-2R}.$$

This gives

$$\frac{1}{u} + \frac{1}{v} = \frac{2}{R},$$

which is exactly the same formula as before. This is only true when exactly the same rule of signs is used. The signs in any mirror problem must be carefully considered twice, namely, when substituting anything into the formula, and after obtaining the solution.

Since f is negative for a convex mirror, v must always be negative (virtual image) when u is positive (real object). The image may, however, be real if the incident rays are converging toward a point close behind the mirror thus giving a negative u or what is called a virtual object.

38. Light-ray Method.—The same results as have been derived in the last two paragraphs may also be derived by applying the laws of reflection to a cone of rays falling on a spherical surface. In this case the normal is drawn to the surface at the point of incidence and the angle of reflection is constructed equal to the angle of incidence in the same plane. For example, Fig. 27

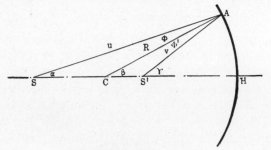

Fig. 27.—Concave mirror.

shows the construction for one of the rays, the plane of incidence being the plane of the paper. SA is a portion of an incident ray the length of which is called u, CA is normal to the spherical surface and has a length R, $S'A$ is a portion of the ray reflected making $\phi' = \phi$ and has the length v. The point S' through which it passes on the axis of the mirror is the image. Call the angles ASH, ACH, and $AS'H$, respectively, α, β, and γ. In the triangle SCA, by the trigonometric law of sines,

$$\frac{\sin \phi}{SC} = \frac{\sin \beta}{u}$$

since

$$\sin (180 - \beta) = \sin \beta.$$

In triangle $S'CA$, similarly,

$$\frac{\sin \phi'}{S'C} = \frac{\sin \beta}{v}.$$

Dividing the above equations gives

$$\frac{S'C}{SC} = \frac{v}{u}$$

or

$$u(S'C) = v(SC),$$

so that

$$u(CH - S'H) = v(SH - CH).$$

Now $CH = R$, and, if the above angles are small, $S'H = v$ and $SH = u$ very nearly so that:

$$u(R - v) = v(u - R)$$

or

$$vR + uR = 2uv.$$

Dividing through by uvR gives

$$\frac{1}{u} + \frac{1}{v} = \frac{2}{R}.$$

39. Images and Magnification.—If an extended object is placed in front of a mirror, each of its points may be considered to be a source, like S in the above, forming an image S' in the mirror. The position of the image built up by these point sources can be found by the aid of the above formula, but it is often well to check the work or to get an approximate solution

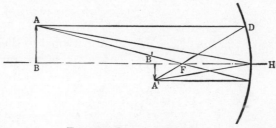

Fig. 28.—Location of image.

by a geometrical construction. In this way, moreover, not only the position but also the size of the image is indicated. The position of any image point can be found by tracing two different rays from the object point and finding where they intersect after reflection. Such rays may be traced by using the law of reflection but it is nearly always more convenient to locate one of the rays or even both of them by using the properties of rays passing through the principal focus. For example, it is known that all rays parallel to the axis are as though coming from a point at infinity and hence are reflected to the principal focus. Consequently, any ray that may be drawn parallel to the axis is reflected through the focus (see Fig. 28). Moreover, a set of rays from the principal focus is reflected as a beam parallel to the axis and hence any single ray through the focus will after reflection be parallel to the axis. Rays of these two types from any object point such as A (Fig. 28) intersect at A' which is the image of

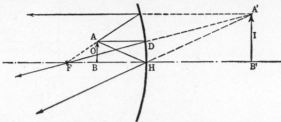

Fig. 29.—Virtual image.

A. Another convenient ray to draw is one reflected at the vertex H of the mirror. Thus one locates $A'B'$, the image of the object AB. The distances BH and $B'H$ are, respectively, equal to u and v in the mirror formula. If O represents the size of the

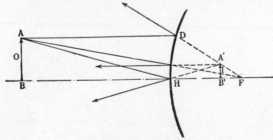

Fig. 30.—Convex mirror.

object and I that of the image, then, since the triangles AHB and $A'HB'$ are similar, the magnification ratio

$$M = \frac{I}{O} = \frac{v}{u}.$$

Exactly the same formula will represent the relative sizes of object and image in any kind of mirror and for any position of object, even if the image is virtual. In case the object is nearer to a concave mirror than the principal focus, the image turns out to be virtual. Figure 29 illustrates the use of the same three kinds of rays to locate the image. When the object is in front of a convex mirror, the image is likewise virtual and is found geometrically as illustrated in Fig. 30. *AD* is a ray parallel to the axis; *AF* is a ray passing through the virtual focus *F* being therefore reflected parallel to the axis; and *AH* is a ray

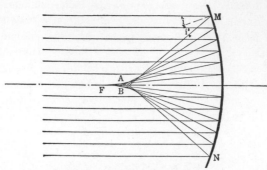

Fig. 31.—Spherical aberration.

to the vertex of the mirror. In all these cases $M = v/u$, as one can easily prove from the above figures.

40. Spherical Aberration.—In case the mirror is not small compared with its radius, as assumed in the preceding derivations of the mirror formula, the image is imperfect. The marginal

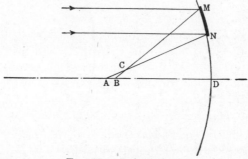

Fig. 32.—Astigmatism.

zones reflect the light rays to a focus which is too close to the mirror, as shown in Fig. 31. This means that the reflected wave is not spherical and so has no definite center. This deviation of the wave from the spherical form is called *spherical aberration*. There is, in this case, concentration of light all along the lines *FA* and *FB* where the rays cross each other forming what is known as a caustic curve. This is the curve seen when light is reflected in a filled cup or a straight-sided glass.

41. Astigmatism.—If a spherical mirror is tilted, the formation of a caustic and the distortion of the image become very noticeable. Light from any point is not reflected to a definite point but to two lines at right angles to each other which are not at the same distance from the mirror. This effect is called astigmatism. The lines are called *focal lines*, and the distance between them is called the *interval of Sturm*. Their formation is best understood by considering the tilted mirror as a portion of a large mirror, such as MN in Fig. 32. It has just been shown that a reflected ray from M will cross a ray from N at a point C before the axis AD is reached. Rotating the figure slightly around this axis, until the line MN sweeps out the area of the small inclined

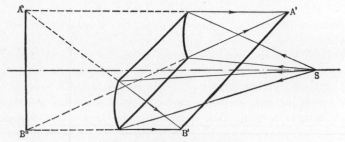

Fig. 33.—Cylindrical mirror.

mirror, will cause the intersection C to trace a short line perpendicular to AB. The rays from the mirror will also cross their rotated counterparts at points along the axis between A and B. Hence AB and the line through C are the two focal lines.

42. Cylindrical Mirror.—The image of a point in a cylindrical mirror likewise consists of two lines at right angles to each other, one of them being real and parallel to the axis of curvature and the other being virtual and at right angles to it. Figure 33 shows how these images are formed by indicating the positions of four representative rays from S. The lines $A'B'$ and $A''B''$ are the two focal lines.

43. Paraboloidal, Ellipsoidal, and Hyperboloidal Mirrors.— A paraboloidal mirror has the important property of being able to focus parallel rays to a point even when it is large. Such mirrors are used in the construction of reflecting astronomical telescopes. The largest telescope of this type in the world is at the Mount Wilson Observatory at Pasadena, California.

It measures 100 inches in diameter. The second largest is the 72-inch reflector at the Dominion Observatory in Canada. Such large mirrors not only reveal fainter objects than a small mirror would show, but also allow finer detail to be visible in star groups, nebulae, surfaces of planets, and satellites.

The converse property of a paraboloidal mirror, namely, of reflecting a parallel beam when the source is at the focus, is utilized in the construction of the most powerful searchlights like those used in lighthouses, aeroplane landing fields, and by the navy.

Ellipsoidal mirrors have the property of reflecting accurately all the rays from a point source at one focus to the other focus of the ellipse. They are used in special apparatus where this property is desired. Surfaces giving such exact foci are said to be *aplanatic*.

Hyperboloidal mirrors are similar in action to the above except that the image is virtual. A source at a focus on one side has a virtual image at the other focus behind the mirror.

It has been shown that a spherical mirror gives a good image only when it is small. If a large mirror is desired it must be made in one of the above shapes. The small spherical mirror is a sort of first approximation for all of these shapes. It must be kept in mind, however, that the focusing is perfect only if the object is a *point* located exactly at the focus. It is physically impossible to produce a perfect image of a large object by a mirror of any shape. For this purpose a spherical mirror is often better than some special form.

Problems

1. What are the position, nature, and size of the image of an object 5 cm. high and (a) 30 cm. in front of a concave mirror with a radius of curvature of 24 cm., (b) 10 cm. in front of the mirror? *Ans.* (a) 20 cm.; $I = 3.33$ cm. real; (b) -60 cm.; $I = 30$ cm. virtual.

2. Show how the above problem may be solved graphically.

3. What are the position, nature, and size of the image of an object 5 cm. high and 10 cm. in front of a convex mirror whose radius of curvature is 24 cm.? *Ans.* 5.46 cm.; $I = 2.73$ cm. virtual.

4. Show how the above problem may be solved graphically

5. An object is placed in front of a concave mirror whose radius of curvature is 24 cm. At what distance from the mirror should it be placed to produce (*a*) a real image four times as large as the object, (*b*) a virtual image five times as large as the object? *Ans.* (*a*) 15 cm.; (*b*) 9.6 cm.

6. A real image is formed by a concave mirror 60 cm. away. If it is four times as large as the object, how far away is the object, and what is the radius of curvature of the mirror? *Ans.* (*a*) 15 cm.; (*b*) 24 cm.

7. Use Huyghens' principle to find the form of the wave reflected from a convex mirror when a convex wave is incident on it.

8. Derive the formula for the radius of the reflected wave, using the diagram pertaining to the above problem.

9. The radius of the eyeball is about 15 mm.; what are the position, nature, and size of the reflected image of an object 10 cm. high and 30 cm. from the eye? *Ans.* —7.3 mm. virtual, 2.4 mm.

10. What must be the radius of curvature of a mirror in order that the image be virtual and one-sixth as large as the object, the object being 15 cm. from the mirror? *Ans.* $R = -6$ cm.

11. What should be the distance of the object from a convex mirror of 30-cm. radius in order to obtain a real image three times as large as the object? Explain the sign of the result. *Ans.* $u = -10$ cm. Virtual object.

CHAPTER VI

REFRACTION

44. Refraction of Light.—The wave theory of light was used in the last chapter to explain the laws of reflection. It can be readily applied to refraction phenomena as well. First of all, the law of refraction will be derived. Let AC (Fig. 34) be a portion of a plane wave incident on the interface of media 1 and 2. Let the angles of incidence and refraction be represented by i and r, respectively, and let V_1 and V_2 be the velocities of light in the two media.

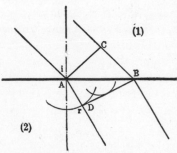

FIG. 34.—Refraction.

While the portion of the wave at C is sending a wavelet to B, the part at A will be sending a wavelet which travels wholly in the second medium to a point D in the same time t. We have then, $CB = V_1t$ while $AD = V_2t$. In half this time, the middle of the incident wave will just reach the interface and will send out a wavelet from the midpoint between A and B with a radius $\frac{1}{2}V_2t$. Similarly, other wavelets can be found and thus the common tangent is found to be a plane. It is perpendicular to the plane of incidence, and its trace is DB. The ray AD is, therefore, in the plane of incidence, since a ray is any perpendicular to a wave. The angle $ABD = r$ and $BAC = i$. We have then

$$CB = V_1t = AB \sin i,$$
$$AD = V_2t = AB \sin r.$$

Dividing we get

$$\frac{\sin i}{\sin r} = \frac{V_1}{V_2} = n_{12},$$

48

where n_{12} is a constant for any two media, being equal to the ratio of the velocities of light, and is called the *index of refraction of the second medium with respect to the first*. If the first medium is a vacuum, then the constant ratio is simply called *the (absolute) index of refraction of the second medium*. Since the absolute index of the first medium is $n_1 = V/V_1$ and the index of the second is $n_2 = V/V_2$, where V is the velocity of light in a vacuum, the relative index n_{12} is therefore equal to the ratio of the index of the second medium to that of the first. That is,

$$n_{12} = \frac{n_2}{n_1}$$

If medium 1 is air, this equation states that the relative index of any medium with respect to air is equal to its absolute index divided by that of air. Since the index of air is 1.00029, which is very close to unity, the index of a substance with respect to air differs by only 0.03 per cent from the absolute index and the two are often used interchangeably as being practically the same.

Table II contains the indices of refraction for a few common substances. These values are for the light of a Bunsen flame charged with the vapor of common salt (the so-called "sodium light"), and for a temperature of 20°C.

TABLE II

Air	1.000292	Glass:	
Acetone	1.359	Boro-sil. crown	1.524
Alcohol, ethyl	1.362	Light flint	1.571
Alcohol, methyl	1.329	Medium flint	1.627
Benzene	1.501	Dense flint	1.754
Bromnaphthalene	1.658	Densest flint	1.963
Canada balsam	1.530	Gold	0.42
Carbon disulphide	1.628	Glycerin	1.473
Chloroform	1.447	Hydrogen	1.000139
Ether, ethyl	1.354	Ice	1.311
Gelatin	1.530	Platinum	2.04
Glass:		Silver	0.18
Ordinary crown	1.516	Water	1.333

It should be noted that the law of refraction is reversible. That is, if the direction of the light is reversed so that the new value of i is the same as the previous value of r, the new value of r is the same as the previous i. Because of this fact, it is best to write the law of refraction in the following form. Let φ_1 be the angle the light ray makes with the normal in the medium 1, regardless of whether it is the angle of incidence or refraction, and let φ_2 be the corresponding angle in the other medium, then the law of refraction becomes

$$\frac{\sin \varphi_1}{\sin \varphi_2} = \frac{V_1}{V_2} = \frac{n_2}{n_1},$$

or

$$n_1 \sin \varphi_1 = n_2 \sin \varphi_2.$$

45. Images in a Medium with a Plane Surface.—It is a matter of common experience that an object immersed in water appears altered in position. The image is closer to the surface, and can

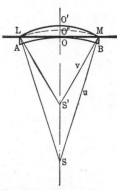

FIG. 35.—Image in a plane surface.

be located by an application of Huyghens' principle. Let S be some point of an object at a distance u below the surface in a medium in which the velocity of light is V_2 (Fig. 35). Let V_1 be the velocity of light in the upper medium and let this be greater than V_2. Take the centers of the wavelets on the line LM. To obtain the proper radii, first assume the medium below to be extended above LM. The wave AOB would then simply expand in the time t to the position indicated by $LO''M$ and the wavelets would be tangent to this wave. In case, however, the velocity above LM were greater, the radii of the wavelets would all be increased in the same ratio and the actual refracted wave would be $LO'M$ with its center at S'. To find its location, it is noted that by Huyghens' construction it follows that

$$OO' = V_1 t \text{ and } OO'' = V_2 t.$$

If the cone of rays from S is narrow (less than 8 degrees) we can regard u and v as the perpendicular distances of S and S' from the surface. In fact, it is only in this case that $LO'M$ can be considered spherical. Putting $LO = y$ we have

$$V_1 t = \frac{y^2}{2v}$$

and

$$V_2 t = \frac{y^2}{2u}.$$

Dividing these into each other gives

$$\frac{u}{v} = \frac{V_1}{V_2} = \frac{n_2}{n_1} = n,$$

where n is the index of the immersing medium with respect to the other. In an optically denser medium (V_1 greater than V_2) the image appears raised. Since the cone of rays that can enter the pupil of the eye is always small at ordinary distances, the assumption of a narrow cone fits this visual case very closely.

As may have been surmised from the above, the restriction of the cone of rays means that otherwise spherical aberration would make the problem of image location more difficult to solve. In fact, there would be no single definite position. In Fig. 36 is shown the refraction of a wide-angle cone of rays at a

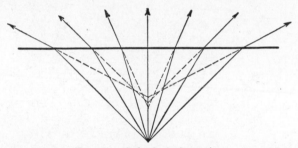

Fig. 36.—Spherical aberration.

plane surface and the formation of a virtual caustic curve. Such a figure is constructed by applying the law of refraction to every ray or by drawing normals to the wave found by Huyghens' principle. The aberration is not noticeable directly to the eye in viewing submerged objects, because the pupil is so small that the cone of rays used is very narrow. The visible effect is to raise and to displace the image still further along the caustic curve as the surface is viewed more and more obliquely. An object of some length, therefore, appears distorted. This discussion of images produced by refraction will be continued in the next chapter under the heading "Lenses."

The position of the image seen perpendicularly to the surface can be used to determine the index of refraction of a plate of any transparent substance. A little lycopodium powder is sprinkled on the stage of a microscope which is of the type provided with a micrometer focusing screw. The microscope is focused on the powder and the micrometer reading observed. The plate is then laid over the stage and the microscope raised until the new focus is obtained. The amount of raising is equal to $u - v$, while the thickness of the plate is u. These data enable one to find the index of refraction.

46. Plane Parallel Plate.—Consider a plate of transparent substance of index n in air, the index of air being approximately

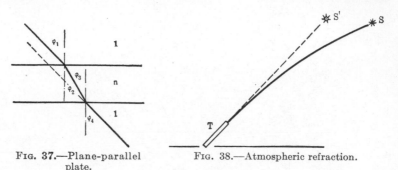

FIG. 37.—Plane-parallel   FIG. 38.—Atmospheric refraction.
plate.

equal to one. If we take the angles of incidence and refraction as indicated in Fig. 37, then

$$1 \times \sin \varphi_1 = n \times \sin \varphi_2, \text{ and } n \times \sin \varphi_3 = 1 \times \sin \varphi_4.$$

If the faces of the plate are parallel, $\varphi_2 = \varphi_3$; consequently $\varphi_1 = \varphi_4$, and therefore the final ray is parallel to the first. All the rays from an object suffer a sidewise displacement; hence the image will likewise appear displaced unless the object is very far away.

Suppose that a large number of plane parallel plates of various substances were laid on top of each other. Let the indices be $n_1, n_2, n_3, \ldots n'$, in succession. Then, step by step,

$$n_1 \sin \varphi_1 = n_2 \sin \varphi_2 = n_3 \sin \varphi_3 \ldots = n' \sin \varphi'.$$

Thus it is seen that for any number of parallel plates the product $n \sin \varphi$ is an "invariant." The direction of the final ray depends only on the natures of the first and the final media and the direction of the incident ray. Any or all of the intermediate media could be left out with the same final result as to direction.

An interesting application of this is found in the problem of astronomical refraction.   Owing to refraction by the atmosphere, the rays from any star are bent downward somewhat as shown in Fig. 38.   This bending must be calculated by astronomers, since it affects the apparent positions of all bodies.   It is not known exactly how the index of refraction of the air varies with altitude, but the indices of space ($n = 1.000000-$) and of air at the earth's surface ($n = 1.00029$) are known very exactly.   The amount of deviation of the light can then be calculated.   The calculations are difficult unless the bodies are nearly overhead.   For objects near the horizon the amount of refraction is of an

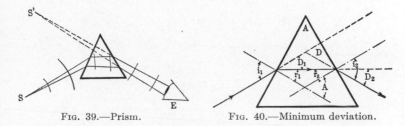

FIG. 39.—Prism.   FIG. 40.—Minimum deviation.

amount such as to cause the sun to be seen just above the horizon when it is entirely just below.

47. Refraction by a Prism.—A solid with plane faces inclined to each other is called a *prism*.   In a prism the refractions at the two surfaces do not annul each other as in a plane parallel plate but give a resultant deviation as shown in Fig. 39.   Rays from a point S are refracted so as to appear to come from a virtual image S'.   The location of this image is found by tracing through any two rays from S and finding where they intersect.   Either the law of refraction or some special geometrical construction equivalent to the same, such as Huyghens' principle, may be used to find refracted rays.

48. Deviation by Prismatic Refraction.—The angular deviation of a ray depends on the angle of incidence and on the material and angle of the prism.   Let A (Fig. 40) be the angle of the prism and let the angle of incidence on the first face be i_1.   Suppose that the external medium is air, the index of which is practically 1.   Let r_1 and r_2 be the angles the refracted ray makes with the normals to the two refracting planes and let i_2 be the final angle of emergence. Then we have by the laws of refraction that $\sin i_1/\sin r_1 = n$ and that $\sin i_2/\sin r_2 = n$. The respective deviations at the two surfaces will be D_1 and D_2, where a consideration of Fig. 40 will show that $D_1 = i_1 - r_1$ and that $D_2 = i_2 - r_2$. The total deviation is the sum of these two, so that $D = D_1 + D_2 = (i_1 + i_2) - (r_1 + r_2)$. The angle of the prism is A and this is equal to $r_1 + r_2$, as is readily seen from the figure. Therefore, $D + A = i_1 + i_2$.

It can be shown either experimentally, or graphically, or by further mathematical analysis that the deviation D is at its minimum when the prism is turned so that $i_1 = i_2$. In this case, $r_1 = r_2$, and

$$A = 2r_1, \text{ and } D + A = 2i_1.$$

Since the ratio of the sines of i_1 and r_1 is the index of refraction of the prism, it follows that

$$n = \frac{\sin i}{\sin r} = \frac{\sin \frac{1}{2}(A + D)}{\sin \frac{1}{2}A}.$$

This is the simplest practical formula giving the index of refraction in terms of quantities which can be measured accurately. It is therefore often used in laboratory measurements of the index of refraction. A prism is mounted on a divided circle and rotated until the deviation of the light is a minimum. The angles D and A are measured and the values substituted in the above formula. The measurements are made with an instrument called the spectrometer (Art. 88).

49. Dispersion.—The index of refraction is found to be different for lights of different color, *i.e.*, of different wave length. Therefore all colors are not deviated through the same angle. If one looks through a prism at a source which emits light consisting of various wave lengths, one sees, instead of a single image of the source, a series of images, each of which corresponds to some particular wave length emitted by that source (see Fig. 41). The difference in deviation is called *dispersion*, while the series of images is called a *spectrum*. In case all wave lengths are present, as in ordinary white light, the infinite number of images of the source appear as a continuous band of color. Since the source always has a finite width, there will always be more or less

overlapping of images by neighboring wave lengths with a consequent loss in purity of color. To obtain the best results, the
source should be a very narrow slit with a light behind it. As
the slit is narrowed the colors become purer although fainter.

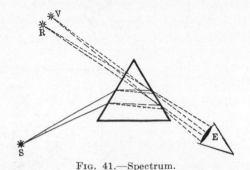

Fig. 41.—Spectrum.

The virtual spectrum produced by a prism and a slit can be
converted into a real spectrum and projected on a screen by
means of a converging lens. The lens (Fig. 42) then serves in
the same capacity as the lens of the eye in Fig. 41 in which the
spectrum is projected directly on the retina.

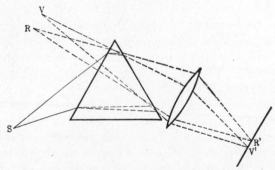

Fig. 42.—Spectrum projected.

50. Fraunhofer Lines.—The spectra of sunlight and of any
ordinary white light appear the same when a broad slit is used.
If, however, the slit is made very narrow, the spectrum of sunlight is seen to be furrowed by a number of fine dark lines or
missing colors, while the spectrum of any other incandescent solid
remains continuous. These lines were first observed by Woll-

aston and later studied by Fraunhofer, who published in 1814 a list of several hundred of them.   Their explanation remained a mystery for nearly 40 years until it was shown that they corresponded in position to the strongly selective absorption by the vapors of some elements.   A few of the lines are due to the absorption by the earth's atmosphere, but most of them must originate on the sun.

The lines represent definite wave lengths.   The most prominent are often used as standards, being denoted by the letters A, $B, C, D, E, F, G, H, I, J, K$, from red to violet.   The most important of these are: the red A line, due to the absorption by oxygen in the earth's atmosphere, the red C line due to hydrogen on the sun, the orange D lines due to sodium vapor on the sun, the blue F line also due to hydrogen, and the violet H and K lines due to calcium vapor.   Their wave lengths are given in the following table.

TABLE III.—WAVE LENGTHS AND COLORS OF PRINCIPAL FRAUNHOFER LINES

	Centimeters	
A	0.00007621	red
C	0.00006563	red
D	0.00005893	orange
E	0.00005270	green
F	0.00004862	blue
H	0.00003969	violet
K	0.00003934	violet

51. Dispersive Power.—For the purpose of this discussion, the dispersion of any two colors will be defined as the difference between their deviations by a prism.   This is the angle between the two rays as they leave the prism.   If the dispersion of prisms made of different materials, but having the same angle, are observed, it is found that the dispersion varies considerably. Newton believed that the dispersion was always proportional to the average deviation, or, that a substance with a high index of refraction would give a proportionately high amount of dispersion. It was first shown by Dollond, in 1757, that this was not true, and that the ratio of dispersion to average deviation varied for different materials.   As a convenient and exact specification of this relation of refraction to dispersion, the *dispersive power* δ of a substance for any two colors, will be defined, *e.g.*, corresponding to the F and C Fraunhofer lines, as the difference between the indices for the two colors $(n_F - n_C)$, divided by the average (or an intermediate) index minus 1, $(n_D - 1)$. That is,

$$\delta = \frac{n_F - n_C}{n_D - 1}.$$

For a very acute prism the quantity so defined is really the ratio of the angular separation of the two colors divided by the average angular deviation. For if A and D are small, it is possible to write without sensible error that

$$n = \frac{A + D}{A} \qquad\qquad \text{(Art. 48)}$$

so that in this case

$$D = (n - 1)A.$$

The angle between the colors F and C will then be

$$D_F - D_C = (n_F - n_C)A.$$

If n_D represents the average index, the average deviation will be

$$D_D = (n_D - 1)A.$$

The ratio between the two is, therefore,

$$\frac{D_F - D_C}{D_D} = \frac{n_F - n_C}{n_D - 1}$$

which is defined as the dispersive power of the substance.

Table IV gives the indices and dispersive powers for a few common substances:

TABLE IV

Substance	n_D	$n_F - n_C$	$\dfrac{n_F - n_C}{n_D - 1}$
Air..........................	1.000292	0.00000295	0.0121
Carbon disulphide...............	1.6276	0.0345	0.0547
Diamond......................	2.4173	0.0254	0.0179
Glass:			
Ordinary crown...............	1.5159	0.0074	0.0141
Light flint....................	1.5710	0.0133	0.0232
Dense flint....................	1.7541	0.0274	0.0364
Densest flint..................	1.9626	0.0488	0.0507
Quartz........................	1.5442	0.0078	0.0129
Water.........................	1.3330	0.0060	0.0180

52. Direct-vision and Achromatic Prisms.—Because of the different dispersive powers of glasses having different chemical compositions, one can secure prisms having the same average deviations but different dispersions. It is therefore possible to combine two such prisms in the manner illustrated in Fig. 43 so as to cancel out the average deviation of the beam of light without canceling out all of the dispersion. Such a prism pair is called a direct-vision prism. The component prisms may be made of crown and flint glasses. In order to obtain the same average deviation, the angle of the crown prism must be made larger. A series of prisms, as shown in Fig. 43, may be designed so as to give a considerable amount of dispersion with no average devia-

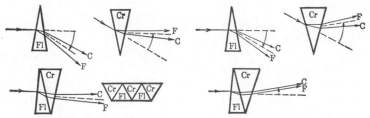

FIG. 43.—Direct-vision prism.   FIG. 44.—Achromatic prism.

tion. This arrangement is very useful at times and is employed in the construction of direct-vision spectroscopes.

The development of glasses with widely different dispersive powers, and other special optical properties is a relatively modern achievement in glass manufacture. Optical glasses, like all others, are mixtures of oxides of silicon, sodium, potassium, calcium, and lead, and often small amounts of other materials (Appendix, Table VII). The composition of the glass is carefully controlled throughout the melting so as to obtain the desired optical properties. Crown glasses contain no lead oxide, while flint glasses do. Sometimes borax or barium oxide is added to get certain properties. Needless to say, the materials must be very pure and especially free from the chemicals which cause color or the decrease in transparency commonly occurring in ordinary glass. In this and other ways, the production of optical glass is a very exacting process.

It is often required to refract a beam of light without producing dispersion. This can also be accomplished by a combination of two prisms made of glasses having different dispersive powers. The angles of the component prisms are in this case chosen so that the dispersions are equal. The deviations will then be necessarily unequal so that if the prisms are combined, as shown in Fig. 44, to neutralize the dispersions, there will be a resultant deviation which will be nearly the same for all colors. The colored rays are displaced sideways by a slight amount, but since they come to the eye in the same direction, they will be focused on the same point of the retina, giving a color-free image.

If the dispersive powers for equal changes in wave length were the same throughout the spectrum, the "achromatism" described above would be perfect for all colors if it amounted to a superposition of any two colors. Because, however, the dispersive power does not quite remain the same in different portions of the spectrum, all of the colors will not quite superpose when two of them do. This leaves a residual "secondary spectrum."

This variation in dispersive power causes parts of spectra produced by prisms of different material to be of different length. Thus, for example, if a prism is constructed of flint glass, which gives the same length of spectrum between the A and K lines as one of crown glass, then it will be found that when these two lines are superposed, the other Fraunhofer lines will not fall exactly over each other.

The fact that it is possible to change the direction of rays by refraction without obtaining dispersion is very important. If it were not possible to do this, lenses could never be used in fine optical instruments, especially when the magnifying power is high, because of the unequal focusing of different colors. In fact, Newton thought this to be the case and considered spherical mirrors to be the most practical means for producing images free from this defect.

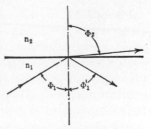

Fig. 45.—Critical angle.

53. Total Reflection.—Suppose that light is passing through two media of indices n_1 and n_2 separated by a plane interface as in Fig. 45. If φ_1 and φ_2 are the respective angles of incidence and refraction, then, according to the law of refraction.

$$\sin \varphi_2 = \frac{n_1}{n_2} \sin \varphi_1.$$

Suppose that n_2 is less than n_1 so that n_1/n_2 is greater than 1. In this case, $\sin \varphi_2$ is always greater than $\sin \varphi_1$ and, hence, φ_2 is greater than φ_1 as shown. As φ_1 is increased there will be reached some value of φ_1 less than 90 degrees for which φ_2 will be just equal to 90 degrees. Beyond this it evidently cannot go and remain a refracted ray. The angle of φ_1 for which this occurs is called the *critical angle* and will be denoted by φ_c. If light is incident at a greater angle than this, there is no refracted ray at all. *All* of the incident light will be reflected back at an angle equal to the angle of incidence, instead of only a part of it as at other angles. This phenomenon is called *total reflection* and occurs for all angles greater than φ_c. This angle can be determined by the equation obtained from the above on putting φ_2 equal to 90 degrees. Hence

$$\sin \varphi_c = \frac{n_2}{n_1}.$$

In case the upper medium is air, then $n_2 = 1$ and $\sin \varphi_c = 1/n_1$. The critical angles for a few common substances when the external medium is air are given below:

Water	48° 36′
Crown glass	43° 2′
Flint glass	37° 34′
Quartz	40° 22′
Diamond	24° 26′

The small critical angle of diamond accounts for its brilliancy which is due to the internal total reflection of light which occurs for a greater variety of angles than in any other substance. The light which enters a diamond is totally reflected back and forth a number of times before emerging and thus produces a set of bright multiple reflections.

Since the index of every substance varies somewhat with wave length, the critical angle will be a little different for the different colors. Violet is totally reflected at a lesser angle than red because of its greater index.

54. The Abbe Refractometers.—The principle of total reflection is often applied to the measurement of indices of refraction, especially of liquids, by measuring their critical angle. The chief advantage of this method is that only a small amount of the substance is necessary. One of the instruments often used, called the *Abbe crystal refractometer*, after its inventor, consists essentially of a hemisphere of dense flint glass on which the substance to be tested is placed as shown in Fig. 46. None of the light incident from the top can be refracted into the sharply bounded region *COB*. This is the converse of the total reflection effect just discussed. The angle *AOB* is the critical angle with respect to the material of the hemisphere since it corresponds to a grazing ray in the

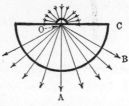

Fig. 46.—Abbe crystal refractometer.

other medium. A telescope mounted on a circle graduated in degrees is used to measure this angle. It follows then, that

$$n_x = n \sin \varphi_c,$$

where n_x is the index of the unknown and n is the index of the glass hemisphere.

When the index of a small plate of solid material, such as a crystal, is measured, it must be stuck to the top surface of the hemisphere with a drop of some oil with a higher index of refraction than that of the unknown plate. The critical angle observed in this case is that of the plate with respect to the glass, since the plane parallel film of oil does not deviate the rays. The formula above will then give the index of the plate.

In a common form of *Abbe refractometer* the liquid whose index is to be measured is placed between two prisms as shown in Fig. 47. The lower prism serves to keep the liquid film in place and to aid in the illumination. When clamped into position,

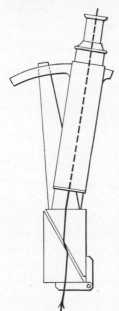

Fig. 47.—Abbe refractometer.

its ground face is 0.1 millimeter from the polished hypotenuse face of the top prism. Light rays which have passed into the upper prism must all have made smaller angles with the normal than the critical angle. A telescope which receives the emerging rays shows a sharp change in intensity at an angle corresponding to the critical angle.   The prisms are rotated so that this boundary falls on an index in the field of the telescope.   Instead of the critical angles being read on the scale of the instrument, the index of refraction is usually given directly.

When solids are to be measured, the lower prism is not used. Optical contact between the solid, which must have one flat and polished face, is obtained by the use of a film of oil of higher index of refraction.   In this case, the light is not totally reflected off the film of oil, but passes into the upper prism as it would if coming directly from the solid.   Thus the index measured is that of the solid.   In all measurements with the refractometer the index of refraction of the substance to be measured must be less than that of the prism.   With heavy flint-glass prisms one can obtain at least a range of 1.3000 to 1.7000.   Refractometers are used in laboratories to test the strength and purity of solutions, or the proportions of two liquids in mixtures, or percentages of foreign substances.

If the lower prism is dispensed with and the upper prism is wholly immersed in the liquid under test, the instrument is called a *dipping refractometer*.

55. Atmospheric Refraction.—A variety of interesting phenomena arise in nature due to refraction by a non-uniform atmosphere.   The most common of these is the shimmering produced by warm air rising through cooler air.   This is especially noticeable in summer as warm air rises from heated rocks or roadways.   The intermingling of warm, and therefore less dense, currents of air with air which is cooler, and therefore denser, causes optical non-uniformity in the medium.   The less dense air has a smaller index of refraction.   The rays are bent away from their straight course, causing a slight apparent displacement of the object.   Since the currents are constantly changing, the apparent position will not be steady.   Owing to alternate focusing and diverging of the rays, the intensity will also change continually.

The twinkling of stars is explained in a similar manner, except that here the refracting filaments are above and far away so that they, as well as the stars, subtend small angles at the eye. The angle subtended by the planets is much larger, so that they appear to shine more steadily through this fine-grained inhomogeneity.

56. Mirage.—On deserts the ground layer of air which is heated by the sand often remains undisturbed as a layer of a less dense medium just above the surface. Such a layer of heated gas produces the illusion of reflection by water which is known as *mirage*. As shown in Fig. 48, light waves may reach the eye in two ways in such a case, the first route being direct and the second by a gradual bending of the wave by the warm air as it comes near the hot surface. The latter beam produces an inverted image similar to that produced by reflection by water.

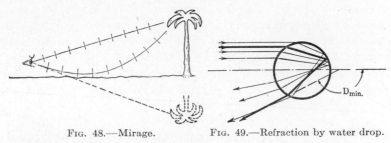

FIG. 48.—Mirage.   FIG. 49.—Refraction by water drop.

57. Refraction of Water Drops.—When the sun shines on a drop of water, one may see all the colors of the rainbow by looking at it from various angles. This is the familiar phenomenon of the colors of dewdrops. To explain it, consider a single spherical drop of water in the practically parallel rays of the sun. An application of the laws of refraction and reflection shows that the refracted light, some of which is reflected at the back surface, as shown in Fig. 49, will emerge inside a cone of a definite aperture. It can be proved that the emergent light is deviated through angles lying between 180 degrees and an angle of minimum deviation which depends on the color. The resulting cone of rays will have an aperture (180 degrees − D) equal to 40 degrees 23 minutes for the violet light and 42 degrees 18 minutes for the red, with the other spectrum colors in between. Now this colored boundary of the cone is formed by rays emerging under the condition of minimum deviation; hence there will be very little divergence of the rays of any one color due to a varying deviation. Therefore the colored boundary is the brightest part of the cone. If the eye is in line with this boundary and is turned toward the drop, the latter will appear brightly colored. The color will be red if the line of sight makes an angle of 42 degrees 18 minutes with the sun's rays, and violet if this angle is 40 degrees 23 minutes.

58. Rainbow.—When the sun shines through falling rain, a bow of color may be seen by looking away from the sun so as to receive the light refracted and reflected by the raindrops in the manner described above. The bow is a circular arc whose

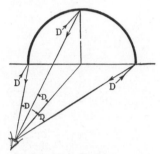

Fig. 50.—Rainbow.

axis is a line through the sun and the observer's eye and whose aperture is about 40 to 42 degrees of arc.

In this case there is a very large number of drops instead of one, and the eye is at some definite fixed point. The sun's rays fall on all the drops in the same direction so that they all send out cones of light with colored rims all pointing the same way. To an observer on the ground (see Fig. 50) only those at an angle such that the eye is in line with the boundary of their color cone will send colored light to the eye. Accordingly, those in a line of sight making an angle of 42 degrees 18 minutes with the direction of the sun's rays will send only red light to the eye. Those at 40 degrees 23 minutes will send only violet. Those below will send only white light of less intensity. The result is a colored bow with violet underneath and red on top.

Often a second bow is seen above the first with the opposite order of colors. This bow is due to light which has been internally reflected twice in the raindrops, as shown in Fig. 51. The minimum deviation of the light rays, which is designated as D, is

greater for the violet rays than for the red. This puts red on the
inside of the reflected cone of light and violet on the outside so
that the red part of the bow is below the blue—just the reverse
of the primary rainbow. Because there are two internal reflections, this bow is not so bright as the primary bow below it. The
angles at which the colors appear, measured from a line through
the eye and parallel to the sun's rays, are 50 degrees 34 minutes
for the red and 54 degrees 4 minutes for the violet.

59. Refraction by Ice Crystals.—Somewhat similar effects
are sometimes produced by ice crystals. These occur in many

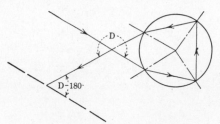

Fig. 51.—Secondary rainbow.

interesting forms but are always such that the elementary unit of
structure is in the form of a hexagonal prism. The refraction
of light through alternate faces of a hexagonal prism is like that
produced by a prism of 60 degrees. As in the case of any other
prism, there is a minimum deviation when the light passage is
symmetrical. It will be recalled that at minimum deviation a
prism may be turned through several degrees without appreciably
changing the direction of the refracted light, while for very
different angles the deviation alters rapidly with prism rotation. A cloud of ice crystals will contain prisms in all possible
orientations. Of all of these, those crystals which are turned so
as to give minimum deviation or are within a few degrees of this
exact orientation, will send light in practically the same direction. There is, therefore, a greater radiation in this direction
than in any other. The angle of minimum deviation of a 60-
degree prism of ice is 22 degrees. Accordingly there will be
more light deflected through 22 degrees than through any other
angle. This causes the halo which is seen at 22 degrees with the
sun or moon when the light passes through a cloud of ice crystals.

If the ice crystals are flat plates with their faces floating horizontally, then when the sun is near the horizon, the refraction will be chiefly to the right and to the left. Thus the light in the halo is especially concentrated at 22 degrees to the right and to the left of the sun. This is the origin of parhelia or "sun dogs."

Halos subtending other angles are produced by refraction through other pairs of prism faces. They are not so common as the above. The small golden ring sometimes seen around the moon is due to a different cause, namely, diffraction of light.

Problems

1. The relative index of refraction of glass with respect to water is 1.150. If the index of water is 1.333, what is the index of the glass? *Ans.* 1.533.

2. A pool of water is 6 ft. deep; how deep does it appear to be if the index is 1.333 and why? *Ans.* 4.5 ft. (see Art. 45).

3. A microscope which is focused on a mark on the stage has to be raised 0.08 cm. to re-focus when a plate of glass 0.25 cm. thick is placed over the mark. What is the index of refraction of the glass? *Ans.* 1.47.

4. What is the angular length of spectrum and average deviation of a glass prism having indices of 1.565 and 1.576 for the red and violet, respectively, and an angle of 5°? *Ans.* (a) 3.3′. (b) 2.85°.

5. The critical angle in a block of glass with respect to air is found to be 45°. What is the index of refraction of the glass? *Ans.* 1.414.

6. The critical angle in glass of index 1.80 with respect to a drop of liquid is 60°. What is the index of the liquid? *Ans.* 1.558.

7. What is the angle of a halo with respect to the sun, produced by refraction of light through faces of ice crystals ($n = 1.31$) which are at an angle of 90°? *Ans.* 45° 44′.

8. Outline three methods by which the index of refraction of a substance can be measured.

9. Prove that $n = \dfrac{\sin (A + D)}{\sin A}$ when the light strikes the first face of a prism at right angles to the surface.

10. A microscope cover glass is 0.1 mm. thick and has an index of refraction equal to 1.5. What change in focusing is made necessary by the presence of the cover glass? *Ans.* 0.033 mm.

11. Show that for an achromatic prism the products of the dispersive powers and the deviations for the two component prisms must be equal to each other.

12. Why is the intensity of the rainbow much greater than that of the white light beneath the bow?

CHAPTER VII

LENSES

60. Types of Lenses.—Even as far back as several thousands of years ago it was known that a piece of clear crystal or glass which was thicker at the center than at the edges, magnified objects seen through it and had the power of concentrating beams of light to a focus. A piece of transparent material with these or similar properties is called a *lens*. The surfaces may have any form, but usually they are spherical. Plane surfaces are included in the above statement, since a plane is a sphere with a very large radius of curvature.

There are six general ways of combining spherical surfaces which are illustrated in the six types of lenses, shown in Fig. 52.

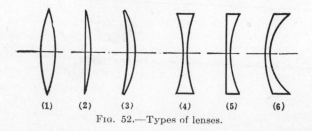

(1) (2) (3) (4) (5) (6)

Fig. 52.—Types of lenses.

The three types which are thicker at the center are called *converging* or *convex* lenses. They tend to make rays converge to a "burning point," or real focus. The lenses which are thinner at the center are said to be *diverging* or *concave*. The three types of converging lenses shown in the figure are (1) biconvex, (2) plano-convex, (3) concavo-convex. The three types of diverging lenses are (4) biconcave, (5) plano-concave, (6) convexo-concave.

61. Refraction at a Convex Surface.—In Fig. 53 is shown a wave IPB in a medium of index n_1 at the moment of incidence on the convex interface JPD between media of index n_1 and n_2. Huyghens' principle is used to find the form JQD of the wave at

67

the moment of complete emergence.   The details of the construction are as applied in Art. 45 to the refraction at a plane surface,
the centers of the wavelets being taken along the refracting
surface JPD and the radii being found by reducing the radii of
wavelets tangent to the form the wave would take if it passed
through without refraction, the reduction being in the ratio of
the velocities of light in the two media.   It is found in this way

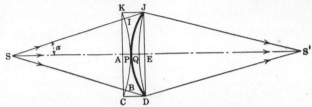

Fig. 53.—Refraction at a convex surface.

that the transmitted wave JQD is spherical if the angle α is
not too large.

If t represents the time taken by the light to travel the distances
IJ and PQ, then

$$t = \frac{IJ}{V_1} = \frac{PQ}{V_2}.$$

Since

$$\frac{V}{V_1} = n_1 \text{ and } \frac{V}{V_2} = n_2,$$

it follows that

$$Vt = n_1 IJ = n_2 PQ.$$

Drawing the lines JK and CD parallel to the axis, and drawing
the chords KAC and JED, then if the angle α is sufficiently small
(about 8 degrees),

$$IJ = KJ = AE \text{ (approximately)},$$

so that

$$n_1 AE = n_2 PQ.$$

Separating these distances into the sagittas of the various arcs,
we have

$$n_1(AP + PE) = n_2(PE - QE)$$

or

$$n_1 AP + n_2 QE = (n_2 - n_1)PE.$$

Using the sagitta formula and letting u be the radius of the incident wave, v the radius of the transmitted wave, R the radius of the surface, and y the half length of each chord, this becomes:

$$n_1 \frac{y^2}{2u} + n_2 \frac{y^2}{2v} = (n_2 - n_1)\frac{y^2}{2R}$$

or

$$\frac{n_1}{u} + \frac{n_2}{v} = \frac{(n_2 - n_1)}{R}.$$

The quantities are positive when as shown in the figure. Thus, for a concave surface, R would be negative as can in fact be shown by deriving the formula for such a surface. The formula applies to each of the surfaces of a lens. It also applies to the refraction at the cornea of the eye. For a plane surface ($R = \infty$) it reduces to the same formula as that derived in Art. 45 for refraction at a plane surface.

62. Optical Path.—In dealing with lenses it will be found convenient to apply the theorem in regard to the equality of the optical paths along any two rays through a lens. Usually the central and marginal rays are selected.

In Fig. 54 is shown a wave, IPB, at the moment of incidence on a biconvex lens and at the moment of emergence, JQD. The

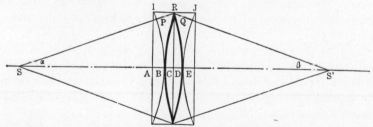

FIG. 54.—Refraction by converging lens.

shape of the emerging wave may be found exactly by applying Huyghens' principle to the passage of the wave through each refracting surface.

Let t be the time taken for the wave to travel from B to D and from P to Q. If V_1 represents the velocity of the light in the external medium and V_2 the velocity in the lens, then

$$BD = V_2 t \text{ and } PRQ = V_1 t.$$

Hence it follows that

$$t = \frac{BD}{V_2} = \frac{PRQ}{V_1}.$$

or

$$n_2 BD = n_1 PRQ = Vt,$$

where n_1 and n_2 are the respective indices of the two media. If the outer medium is air, then n_1 is, of course, put equal to 1. In general, the distance d in any material multiplied by the index n is called the *optical path* and, as shown above, is proportional to the time taken for light to travel that distance. In fact, it is equal to the velocity of light in space multiplied by the time t, so that the optical path nd is equal to the distance the light would travel in a vacuum, or approximately through air, in the time t. For this reason, it is often called the *equivalent air path*.

63. Conjugate Focal Relation.—Consider the case of a biconvex lens with a point object at a distance u from the lens on its principal axis of symmetry as shown in Fig. 54. As explained above, such a lens with a thicker central portion retards the Huyghens' wavelets through the center so that the emerging wave has its curvature changed. Huyghens' construction, as well as experiment, shows that if the aperture is not over 8 degrees, the emerging wave is practically spherical. It then converges to a point at its geometrical center S' at a distance v from the lens.

Suppose that the medium surrounding the lens is air ($n_1 = 1$) and suppose that the index of the glass is n. The time taken for light to travel through the glass BD is equal to the time taken for the light to travel through air from P to Q as explained above. Therefore, the optical paths are equal; that is,

$$PRQ = nBD.$$

If the angle α is not too large it can practically be assumed that the light travels parallel to the axis along IRJ instead of along PRQ. Then

$$IRJ = nBD.$$

Separating the terms on both sides into the sagittas of the various arcs shown in Fig. 54 gives or

$$AB + BC + CD + DE = nBC + nCD$$

$$AB + DE = (n - 1)(BC + CD).$$

Now if the radius of the incident wave is u and that of the emerging wave is v and if r_1 and r_2 are the radii of curvature of the front and back surfaces, respectively, and y is equal to CR, then

$$\frac{y^2}{2u} + \frac{y^2}{2v} = (n - 1)\left(\frac{y^2}{2r_1} + \frac{y^2}{2r_2}\right)$$

or

$$\frac{1}{u} + \frac{1}{v} = (n - 1)\left(\frac{1}{r_1} + \frac{1}{r_2}\right) = \frac{1}{f}.$$

This is the formula expressing the relation between conjugate foci at distances u and v from the lens. If the object is very far away, $v = f$, so that f is the distance from the lens to the point to which parallel rays are focused. It corresponds to a similar quantity defined in Art. 36 and is called the *focal length* of the lens.

In this derivation, u, v, r_1, and r_2 have all been taken as positive when the surfaces of which they are the radii are curved in the manner shown in Fig. 54. If any of these surfaces should be turned oppositely with respect to the direction of the incident light, as they often are, the values of the radii must be given a negative sign when substituted in the above formula. Similarly, if on solving for one of them, it comes out negative, as v, for example, when u is less than f, it means that the direction in which that quantity is to be measured is opposite to that shown in Fig. 54. Thus the transmitted wave is diverging, and the image is virtual in this case.

The same formula will apply to any of the six types of lenses if the same rule of signs is used. To show this, the formula for a diverging lens is derived below. Equating the optical paths through the edge and the center of the lens (Fig. 55), it is found that

$$nAE = BC + nCD + DF,$$

or

$$nAC + nCD + nDE = AC - AB + nCD + DE + EF,$$

giving

$$AB - EF = (n - 1)(-AC - DE).$$

Substituting u, v, r_1, and r_2, with due regard to their signs gives

$$\frac{y^2}{2u} + \frac{y^2}{2v} = (n - 1)\left(\frac{y^2}{2r_1} + \frac{y^2}{2r_2}\right)$$

or

$$\frac{1}{u} + \frac{1}{v} = (n - 1)\left(\frac{1}{r_1} + \frac{1}{r_2}\right).$$

64. Center of a Lens.—In any lens there are always some rays that emerge parallel to their original direction.   These are called

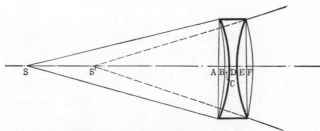

FIG. 55.—Refraction by diverging lens.

principal rays and they determine what are called *secondary axes* of the lens, the principal axis being a line through the centers of curvature of the lens faces.   If the lens is thin, there is a slight sidewise displacement of the principal ray which, however, is often negligible.   For a thick lens, the displacement may be considerable; in fact the theory is not so simple as that given above. It can be shown that in any case, all principal rays pass through a fixed point B (Fig. 56) on the principal axis of the lens.   Let C_1 and C_2 be the centers of curvature of the two surfaces.   From them draw r_1 and r_2, any two parallel radii.   The refraction producing the refracted ray ABC will be like one given by a plane parallel plate, since the surfaces at A and C are parallel to each other by construction, and hence the ray ABC makes equal angles with the normals.   Consequently, the incident and emergent rays will be parallel.   It will be shown that any such undeviated ray, at any angle whatsoever will pass through the same point B on the axis.   Because the radii are parallel, the triangles ABC_1 and

CBC_2 are similar, so that

$$\frac{C_2B}{BC_1} = \frac{C_2C}{C_1A} = \frac{r_2}{r_1}.$$

Since r_1 and r_2 are fixed quantities, this ratio determines the position of B between C_1 and C_2, this being such that it divides the distance C_1C_2 in the given ratio. This ratio is the same no

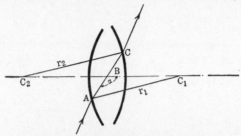

Fig. 56.—Optical center of a lens.

matter what the angle of the principal rays may be. Hence B is the crossing point for all principal rays. If the lens is thin, B may be taken to coincide with the geometrical center, and the sidewise displacement of the rays may be neglected.

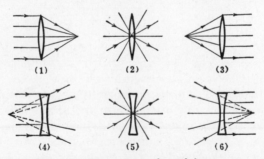

Fig. 57.—Ray passage through lenses.

65. Graphical Determination of the Image.—It has been shown that there is a definite image position for each object point which may be found by solving

$$\frac{1}{u} + \frac{1}{v} = \frac{1}{f},$$

when used with the proper signs. There is also a definite magnification for each object and image distance. This can be derived by means of a geometrical construction of the image. The most convenient rays to trace through the lens in order to find the image are indicated by the ray bundles of Fig. 57. The lens will be assumed very thin so that the principal rays may be drawn undeviated. In the first place, rays parallel to the principal axis on the object side will all be refracted through the principal focus F' as shown in (1) and (4). Secondly, rays

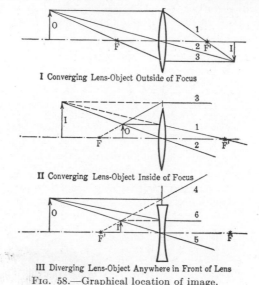

I Converging Lens-Object Outside of Focus

II Converging Lens-Object Inside of Focus

III Diverging Lens-Object Anywhere in Front of Lens

FIG. 58.—Graphical location of image.

through the optical center are undeviated, *e.g.*, (2) and (5). If a third ray is desired, one may use any ray through or toward the principal focus on the object side which will be refracted parallel to the axis, *e.g.*, (3) and (6). As shown in this figure, the relative positions of the two focal points on the two sides of a diverging lens are reversed, the distances to the lens being negative. The application of these rays to the location of the image in a few standard cases is shown in Fig. 58, the numbers on the rays corresponding to the numbers used in Fig. 57.

It will be seen from these diagrams that the object and image always subtend the same angle at the lens. Their sizes are, therefore, proportional to their respective distances from the lens. Therefore the magnification is given by the formula:

$$M = \frac{I}{O} = \frac{v}{u}.$$

66. Object and Image Relation.—The image locations for various positions of the object as well as the sizes of the images are most conveniently obtained by a variation of the graphical construction of the preceding paragraph. Suppose an object of some definite height, perpendicular to the axis, is moved from a great distance (infinity) toward the lens. Let this be a converging lens with foci F and F', as in Fig. 59A. One of the focal points

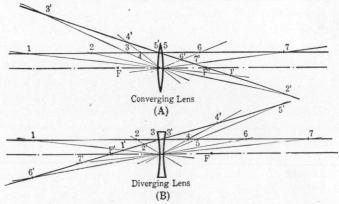

Converging Lens
(A)

Diverging Lens
(B)

Fig. 59.—Dependence of size and position of image on position of object.

is primed to distinguish it from the other, since this is often necessary, as a comparison of the first and last constructions of Fig. 58 will show. As the object is moved toward the lens its top will successively touch the points 1, 2, 3, 4, etc., and these will produce images 1′, 2′, 3′, 4′, etc. The ray parallel to the axis along which the top of the object moves is refracted in the direction 5′F'. The image of any point on the first ray lies on 5′F' at its intersection with a ray through the center of the lens. Some of these rays are also shown in the figure. It will be observed that object points to the right of the lens are also considered. These are "virtual objects," since the light rays coming from the left do not actually cross at these points. These points are foci (images) by other lenses not shown in the figure. The corresponding values of u are negative. It will also be noticed that as the object moves from infinity to the lens and beyond, the image moves in the same direction starting from the principal focus F'. When the object reaches F, the image is at infinity on the image side and when the object gets nearer than F, the image becomes a virtual image on the other side of the lens. The image always moves in the same direction as the object except for the infinite jump when the object is near the front focal point. The displacements of the image points from the axis of the lens give the sizes of the images for an object whose other extremity lies on the axis.

A similar diagram can be drawn for a diverging lens, as shown in Fig. 59*B*. In this case, F' is in front of the lens.

67. Measurement of Focal Lengths.—The determination of the focal length of a thin converging lens of moderate power is relatively easy. The position of the image for some definite position of the object may be found and f calculated by its relation to u and v. On an optical bench of 1 meter in length this is easily carried out if the focal length of the lens is less than 25 centimeters but if it is not too small. Lenses of longer focal length would not give a real image on such a bench because the shortest distance between the object and its real image is four times the focal length of the lens. This can be proved either experimentally or mathematically. When the object and image are closest together u equals v, so that

$$\frac{1}{u} + \frac{1}{u} = \frac{2}{u} = \frac{1}{f},$$

or

$$u = v = 2f,$$

and

$$d = u + v = 4f,$$

where d is the distance between the object and image. When the image and object are this distance apart, the lens is exactly halfway between them. If the object and the screen on which the image is projected are farther apart than $4f$, one can find two positions of the lens between them, both of which will give a real image. If one measures the values of u and v for these two cases one finds that the new v is the same as the old u, and the new u is the old v.

When a lens of long focal length is to be measured, it is customary to use an extra lens in combination with it. This keeps the image within the range of the optical bench. Likewise, a diverging lens may have its focal length measured by the use of a converging lens sufficiently strong to make the final image real. The arrangement of the lenses in such cases is as shown in Fig. 60, the light from the first lens being intercepted by the second. The "object" used with the second lens is a virtual one (negative u), being really the image projected by the first lens toward the point

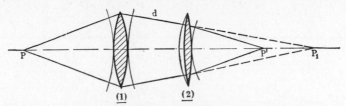

Fig. 60.—Refraction by two lenses.

a distance u behind the lens to be tested. This distance u can be measured by temporarily removing the second lens and measuring the distance to the image by the first lens, which can then be located easily. On replacing the second lens, the distance to the resulting image is measured. Both of these distances are measured from the location of the second lens and give respectively, the magnitudes of u and v. The focal length is then given by the lens formula, in which u has a negative value because the object is virtual.

68. Combinations of Lenses.—The cases just mentioned deal with combinations of two lenses. In general, if a thin lens of focal length f_2 be placed at a distance d from a thin lens of focal length f_1, as is shown in Fig. 60; then, for the first lens

$$\frac{1}{u_1} + \frac{1}{v_1} = \frac{1}{f_1}, \tag{1}$$

and for the second, likewise,

$$\frac{1}{u_2} + \frac{1}{v_2} = \frac{1}{f_2}. \tag{2}$$

The object P is at a distance u_1 in front of the first lens, the first image being at some distance v_1. This means that the radius of curvature of the wave just emerging from the first lens after refraction is v_1. The radius of curvature of the wave incident on the second lens will therefore be $v_1 - d = -u_2$, the negative sign of u_2 being in accordance with our convention of signs. Using this value of u_2, the lens formula (2) may be applied to obtain v_2, which locates the image with respect to the second lens. To find its size, the magnification formula is applied twice, in other words

$$\frac{I}{O} = \frac{v_2}{u_2} \cdot \frac{v_1}{u_1}.$$

The case of two thin lenses touching each other ($d = 0$) is a special case of importance. Such a combination is called a doublet and may be considered to be a thin lens if its components are very thin. One can then put $u_1 = u$, $v_2 = v$, and $d = 0$. Making these substitutions in equations (1) and (2) and adding, it is found that, since $v_1 = -u_2$, $1/v_1$ cancels and consequently

$$\frac{1}{u} + \frac{1}{v} = \frac{1}{f_1} + \frac{1}{f_2}.$$

The quantity on the left must be the reciprocal of the focal length of the doublet, $1/f$, since it is the value of $1/v$ when $u = \infty$. Therefore

$$\frac{1}{f} = \frac{1}{f_1} + \frac{1}{f_2}.$$

69. Strength of a Lens.—In the discussion of lenses the reciprocal of the focal length appears very often. It is usually referred to as the strength or power of the lens. In particular, the reciprocal of the focal length in meters is called the power of the lens in *diopters*. Conversely, the reciprocal of the power in diopters is the focal length in meters. A *plus* lens is a converging lens and a *minus* lens is diverging. Thus, for example, a $+0.2D$ lens is a converging lens having a focal length of 5 meters. This terminology is much used in designating the strengths of spectacle lenses. It will be observed that when thin lenses are combined in contact, the strengths are additive, for

$$\frac{1}{f_1} + \frac{1}{f_2} = \frac{1}{f};$$

hence

$$D_1 + D_2 = D.$$

70. Thick Lenses.—The theory given in the preceding pages applies only to single thin lenses, in which the thickness is negligible in comparison with u, v, and f. The general relation between the object and image distances for any lens, whether thick or thin, may be calculated by applying the formula for refraction at a convex surface (Art. 61) to each of the surfaces. Thus for the front surface of a biconvex lens of index n in air, we have

$$\frac{1}{u_1} + \frac{n}{v_1} = \frac{(n-1)}{r_1}.$$

Similarly for the back surface

$$\frac{n}{u_2} + \frac{1}{v_2} = \frac{(1-n)}{-r_2},$$

since the first index is now n and the radius of the surface is negative. If the two surfaces are a distance d apart, then

$$-u_2 = v_1 - d,$$

as in Art. 68 on the combination of lenses. Substituting this for u_2 in the second equation, and adding, it is found that

$$\frac{1}{u_1} + n\left(\frac{1}{v_1} - \frac{1}{v_1 - d}\right) + \frac{1}{v_2} = (n-1)\left(\frac{1}{r_1} + \frac{1}{r_2}\right).$$

If the lens is thin, that is to say, if d is negligible in comparison with v_1, then this reduces to the ordinary thin lens formula

$$\frac{1}{u} + \frac{1}{v} = \frac{1}{f}$$

otherwise it is evident that this simple formula will no longer apply. However, this formula may be used for thick lenses if the distances u, v, and a modified f, are measured not from the faces or even the center of the lens, but from two fixed points usually inside the lens. Object distances are measured from one of them, P (Fig. 61), while image distances are measured

Fig. 61.—Thick lenses and location of principal points.

from the other P'. These points are called the *principal points* of the lens. In dealing with thick lenses not only the focal lengths but also the locations of the principal points must be known. Their locations in some common types of lenses are outside the lens, as shown in Fig. 61. By a thick lens is meant not only a single lens which is thick, but also any combination of thin lenses when it is regarded as a single compound lens.

The planes passing through the principal points perpendicular to the principal axis are usually called *unit planes*, the principal points being often called *unit points*. This is because any point in one of the unit planes has its image in the other at the same distance from the axis; in other words, there is unit magnification with erect image for these two conjugate planes. The unit planes may be either inside or outside the lens. Two other points, called the *nodal* points, are often defined. They are two points on the principal axis at such places that a ray directed toward one of them emerges in a line passing through the other at the same angle with the axis; in other words, these are the conjugate foci for unit angular magnification. The secondary axes pass through the nodal points and that is their principal use. If there is the same medium on both sides of the lens, the unit points and nodal points coincide. This is usually the case.

In the case of a biconvex lens of thickness d, the unit points are at distances of $\frac{1}{3}d$ from the faces of the lens. Accordingly they are closer to the center of the lens than to the faces. For this reason one usually measures u and v from the center of a moderately thick lens. In really thick lenses even this procedure leads to too much error.

In the case of thick lenses it usually is easier to locate the principal foci than to find the unit points. In such cases it is preferable to transform the lens formula into one which gives the positions of the object and image in terms of their distances from the principal foci. Let f be the front (*i.e.*, object side) focal length and x the distance of the object from the front focus. Let f' be the back focal length and let x' be the distance of the image from the back focus (*i.e.*, on the image side). The distances x and x' are positive when measured from the focus away from the lens. Then $u = f + x$ and $v = f' + x'$. In the most general case of different media on both sides of a lens, the lens formula has the form

$$\frac{f}{u} + \frac{f'}{v} = 1$$

(see Problem 10).   This reduces to the Newtonian form

$$xx' = ff'$$

when the quantities x and x' are introduced.

In order to obtain the magnification formula, the image is located by the tracing of parallel and focal rays.   Referring to Fig. 58 it can be shown by means of similar triangles that:

$$M = \frac{I}{O} = \frac{f}{x} = \frac{x'}{f'}.$$

This magnification formula is usually used in the measurement of focal lengths of thick lenses.   If one determines the magnification M_1 for some position x'_1 of the image and then moves the object and measures the shift in the image $x'_2 - x'_1 = D$ and also the new magnification M_2, then $M_2 - M_1 = \frac{x'_2}{f'} - \frac{x'_1}{f'} = \frac{D}{f'}$

or

$$f' = \frac{D}{M_2 - M_1}.$$

Knowing f' and the magnification, it is possible to work back and locate the principal foci and the unit points.

In the case of a photographic or similar lens, it is convenient to measure f by first making the object distance such that $M_1 = 1$. Then if the object is moved until $M_2 = 2$, the change in distance between the lens and the ground glass gives the focal length directly.

71. Aberrations of Lenses.—In the discussion of lenses, we have regarded (1) the aperture of the lenses to be small, (2) the inclined cones of rays to focus as perfectly as the axial, and (3) the index of refraction to be a definite constant (independent of color).   This was done for the purpose of simplifying the first discussion, and because the results so obtained hold for the perfect or ideal lens.   Actually there is no perfect single lens, and often cases arise when the defects must be considered and eliminated. Any instrument of high magnifying power would, in fact, be worthless if the defects of the individual lenses were not balanced so as to give a perfect or near enough perfect combination.   The greatest number of defects or "aberrations" considered in the

design of the finest lenses is nine.   There are, however, three of
these which are more important than the rest, and only these will
be considered here.   These are suggested by the three approxi-
mations mentioned at the beginning of this paragraph.   They are
called (1) *spherical aberration*, (2) *astigmatism, and* (3) *chromatic
aberration.*

72. Spherical Aberration.—If the diameter of a lens is not
small compared with its focal length, the refracted waves will not
be exactly spherical even for object points on the axis.   In
this case, there will be no definite point focus for all the rays.
This effect is called spherical aberration.   It was left out of
consideration in the preceding theory by taking a lens with so
small an aperture that all the rays could be considered as traveling practically parallel to the axis, as *PQ*, in Fig. 62, instead of

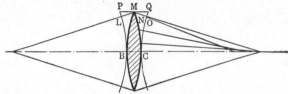

Fɪɢ. 62.—Spherical aberration.

LMN.   For an aperture angle of only 8 degrees or less this
assumption leads to an error of less than 1 per cent, becoming
greater with increasing angle.   A formula for the radius of the
refracted wave was derived by taking *PQ* equal to *nBC*, thus
locating *Q* with reference to *P* and determining the radius of
curvature, *v*, of the reflected wave.   Now the distance *nBC* is
really to be measured in the direction of *LMN* and will reach to
some point *O* so that *LMNO* is the actual distance traveled in
air during the time the center travels from *B* to *C*.   Referring
to the figure, it is seen that *LMN* is less than *PQ* so that *O* will lie
beyond *N* as shown, and the refracted wave will really be more
strongly curved than it was considered to be.   As points farther
from the axis are taken, the increased curvature will be more
marked while for points near the axis the assumptions previously
made will be justified.   These outer zones of the wave which
are more sharply curved will focus closer to the lens, in fact,
along a caustic curve with its tip at the focus of the central rays.

73. Reduction of the Spherical Aberration.—Since the marginal rays in a lens undergo too great a deviation, anything which will diminish the deviation will reduce the amount of spherical aberration. Since the portions of a lens are equivalent to prisms, the lens faces can be so curved that the light passage through them will be symmetrical. The deviation will then be a minimum as in the case of a prism and the desired end will thus be accomplished. For this reason plano- and concavo-convex lenses are often used instead of the biconvex form. Much improvement may be obtained with a plano-convex lens turned in the right way. This is shown in Fig. 63. It is easy to see that the rays in *B* pass through the lens more symmetrically than in *A*.

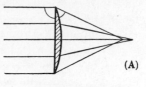

(A)

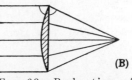

(B)

FIG. 63.—Reduction of spherical aberration.

74. Aberration-free Points of a Sphere.—There is one important exception to the general rule that a cone of rays must be narrow in order that refraction at a spherical surface be free

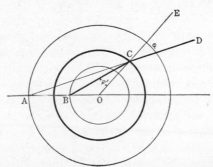

FIG. 64.—Aberration-free points of a spherical lens.

from spherical aberration. This will, however, only occur when the object and image are respectively at certain definite points called aberration-free points. Any sphere has a pair of such points which may be found by a geometrical construction first given by Weierstrass. Consider a sphere of radius *r* and index *n* surrounded by air (index = 1). Draw two concentric circles with radii *nr* and *r/n*. The intersections of any diameter with these two circles are aberration-free points, *e.g.*, points A and B in Fig. 64. This is proved by showing that any ray from one of them, say BC, will, after refraction, coincide with CD whose projection passes through A. The directions of BC and CD with respect to the normal to the surface, a radius OC, must satisfy the law of refraction, namely,

$$\frac{\sin \phi}{\sin \phi'} = n.$$

To show that they do, proceed as follows: The triangle AOC is similar to the triangle BOC because the angle O is common to both of them and because the sides are in the ratio

$$\frac{OC}{OB} = \frac{AO}{CO} = n$$

by construction. Therefore the angles OBC and ϕ are equal. The sine law of trigonometry gives

$$\frac{\sin \phi}{\sin \phi'} = \frac{OC}{OB} = n,$$

which proves the proposition that BC and ACD as drawn above obey the law of refraction. Since C was any point on the sphere, this proves that any ray BC is refracted so that its projection passes through A. Therefore A is a virtual image of B and is free from spherical aberration. This principle is applied in the construction of immersion lenses for microscopes. The lens is in the form of a hemisphere and the object is immersed in oil of the same index as the lens. This is equivalent to imbedding the object in a sphere of index n. The image obtained at A, when the object is at B, is magnified and free from spherical aberration.

75. Astigmatism.—If a lens gives an image on its axis which is free from spherical aberration, it does not necessarily mean that the image of a point not on the axis will be perfect. Waves from such points strike the lens obliquely and are, as a matter of fact, refracted so as to possess different curvatures in two directions at right angles, one of these principal directions being in the plane containing the ray and the principal axis. Such a wave is shown in Fig. 65, where sections parallel to arcs 1-2 and 3-4, at right angles to the paper, have a greater curvature than sections parallel to 1-4 and 2-3. The rays in the former sections will come to a focus along a vertical line 1,2-3,4, while the latter rays will come to a focus along 1,4-2,3 farther back and perpendicular to the first. These lines are called focal lines and are the astigmatic images of the point source. Such astigmatic images always result from oblique refraction by ordinary lenses. In some types of lenses this is very objectionable and must be removed by compounding with lenses of different types of glass

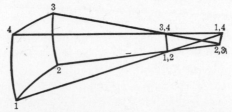

Fig. 65.—Astigmatic foci of a non-spherical wave.

with curvatures designed so as to neutralize their astigmatism. Such combinations of lenses are said to be anastigmatic. They are much used in photography.

Cylindrical lenses illustrate the extreme case of astigmatic lenses. They are often used to magnify lines on scales where only one dimension need be magnified, namely the distance between the lines. A wave falling on such a lens converges only in the direction of a line normal to the axis of the cylindrical curvature. In azimuths at right angles, the effect is like that of a plane parallel plate.

Astigmatic lenses are used to correct for astigmatism of the eye. Such spectacle lenses are lenses with one surface spherical and the other one either cylindrical or toric. A *toric* surface is one which has the shape obtained by rotating a circular arc about a line not passing through its center of curvature. Such sphero-cylindrical and sphero-toric lenses have different powers in the two principal meridians of maximum and minimum curvature. The powers can be expressed in diopters as before.

In case the two surfaces are ground prismatically, there is a deviation of the principal rays and, therefore, of the image. The power of this prismatic effect in *prism diopters* is the deviation of the light in centimeters at a distance of one meter. For prisms of small angle this is roughly equal to the angle of the prism in degrees.

76. Chromatic Aberration.—The third defect of lenses mentioned above was the effect due to the variation of the index of refraction with wave length. Since the focal length of a lens depends on the value of n, it is evident that it must be different for different colors. The expression for the focal length may be written in the form

$$\frac{1}{f} = (n - 1)K,$$

where K is written for the part of the expression that depends only on the shape of the lens. Hence K is a geometrical constant, while n is a physical constant depending on certain physical properties of the glass. Since n is greater for violet light than for red, the focal length must be less and the violet rays bent closer to the lens, as shown in Fig. 66. By cementing to such a

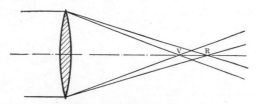

Fig. 66.—Chromatic aberration.

lens a diverging lens of equal dispersion but smaller power, it is possible to neutralize the dispersion without eliminating the converging power entirely. Such a second correcting lens must be made of glass having a greater dispersive power if one desires a converging combination. Hence, the diverging lens would in this case be made of flint glass and the converging lens of crown glass. The combination is called an achromatic doublet. The relations which must exist between the dispersive powers and the focal lengths are not very hard to derive.

Suppose that it is desired to focus F (blue) light together with C (red) light. F and C are two Fraunhofer lines. For the first lens

$$\frac{1}{f'_C} = (n'_C - 1)K' \text{ and } \frac{1}{f'_F} = (n'_F - 1)K'.$$

For the second

$$\frac{1}{f''_C} = (n''_C - 1)K'' \text{ and } \frac{1}{f''_F} = (n''_F - 1)K''.$$

For the combination, since

$$\frac{1}{f} = \frac{1}{f'} + \frac{1}{f''},$$

$$\frac{1}{f_C} = (n'_C - 1)K' + (n''_C - 1)K'',$$

and

$$\frac{1}{f_F} = (n'_F - 1)K' + (n''_F - 1)K''.$$

The focal lengths of the combination for these two colors are equal when:

$$\frac{1}{f_C} = \frac{1}{f_F}$$

or

$$(n'_F - n'_C)K' + (n''_F - n''_C)K'' = 0.$$

Now

$$K' = \frac{1}{f'_D(n'_D - 1)},$$

and

$$K'' = \frac{1}{f''_D(n''_D - 1)}.$$

Substituting in the above gives

$$\frac{\delta'}{f'} + \frac{\delta''}{f''} = 0,$$

where δ' and δ'' are the respective dispersive powers, and f' and f'' are the focal lengths of the lenses for some average wave length (D, for example). The resultant focal length of the doublet is given by

$$\frac{1}{f} = \frac{1}{f'} + \frac{1}{f''}.$$

If one has at his disposal two kinds of glass of known dispersive powers and desires to construct an achromatic doublet having any focal length f, the last two equations above will enable him to determine the focal lengths of the lens components.

Chromatic aberration may also be reduced by the use of two thin converging lenses at a distance apart equal to half the sum of their focal lengths. This kind of combination is often used, especially in eyepieces of optical instruments. If the focal lengths are equal, it is easier to see the truth of the above statement although it is perfectly general. In such a case the first lens will be at the principal focus of the second and so the dispersed rays from any point of the first lens will be made parallel by the second, as shown in Fig. 67. The eye will focus all such

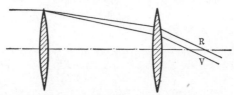

Fig. 67.—Partial correction of chromatic aberration.

parallel rays to the same point on the retina and so a white image will be seen.

Problems

1. Find the position, nature, and size of the image of an object 8 cm. high and at a distance of (a) 32 cm. and (b) 16 cm. from a converging lens whose focal length is 20 cm. *Ans.* (a) $v = 53.3$ cm.; real; $I = 13.3$ cm.; (b) $v = -80$ cm.; virtual; $I = 40$ cm.

2. Solve Problem 1 if the lens is diverging. *Ans.* (a) $v = -12.3$ cm.; virtual; $I = 3.08$ cm.; (b) $v = -8.88$ cm.; virtual; $I = 4.44$ cm.

3. Show by means of diagrams how the above problems may be solved graphically by tracing rays through the lens.

4. An image five times as large as the object is projected on a screen 5 m. away from the lens. What is its focal length? *Ans.* 83.4 cm.

5. The radii of curvature of the faces of a thin lens are 50 and 20 cm. and the index of refraction is 1.52. What is the focal length of the lens if it is (a) biconvex; (b) concavo-convex; (c) biconcave; (d) convexo-concave? *Ans.* (a) 27.6 cm.; (b) 64.1 cm.; (c) −27.6 cm.; (d) −64.1 cm.

6. Show that there must be, in general, between an object and a screen on which its image is projected, two points at which the lens may be placed. Show also that the square root of the product of the sizes of the images in the two cases is equal to the size of the object.

7. Two converging lenses, respectively 15 and 20 cm. in focal length, are placed 5 cm. apart. What are the nature, size, and position of the image of an object 5 cm. high at a distance of 10 cm. from the first lens? *Ans.* Real; $I = 20$ cm.; $v_2 = 46.67$ cm.

8. Derive the relation between the position of the image and object in the case of a biconvex lens of index n immersed in a liquid of index n'.

Ans. $\dfrac{1}{u} + \dfrac{1}{v} = \dfrac{n - n'}{n'} \left(\dfrac{1}{r_1} + \dfrac{1}{r_2} \right)$.

9. If the focal length of a lens whose index is 1.52, is 50 cm. in air, what is the focal length in water (index = 1.33)? *Ans.* 182 cm.

10. If a lens is cemented over an opening into a tank containing some liquid, what formula will give the object and image relation? Show that the focal length will have two different values depending on the direction of the light. *Ans.* $\dfrac{n_a}{u} + \dfrac{n_l}{v} = (n_g - n_a) \dfrac{1}{r_1} + (n_g - n_l) \dfrac{1}{r_2}$. Let $u = \infty$ and solve for v, thus obtaining the "back focal length" f'; then let $v = \infty$ and similarly obtain the "front focal length" f. The lens formula can then be written in the form: $\dfrac{f}{u} + \dfrac{f'}{v} = 1$.

11. Show that the optical paths from an object point to the corresponding image point along *any* two paths through the lens are equal. (Assume no spherical aberration.)

12. The radii of curvature of a concavo-convex lens are, respectively, 60 and 30 cm., and the index of refraction is 1.55. What are the location, nature, and size of the image of an object 10 cm. high and 20 cm. from the lens? *Ans.* $v = -24.4$ cm., virtual, $I = 12.2$ cm.

13. An image eight times as large as the object is projected on a screen 1 m. from the lens. What is the power of the lens in diopters? *Ans.* 9 diopters.

14. A lens projects a real image with unit magnification. When the object is altered in position so as to make the image twice as large, the image is 10 cm. farther from the lens than it was before. What is the focal length of the lens? *Ans.* 10 cm. $(v_2 - v_1 = 3f - 2f = 10)$.

15. It is desired to construct an achromatic lens having a power of 4 diopters. The two kinds of glass to be used have their dispersive powers respectively equal to 0.0141 and 0.0364. What should be the focal lengths of the two component lenses? *Ans.* $+15.3$ cm. and -39.5 cm.

CHAPTER VIII

OPTICAL INSTRUMENTS

77. The Eye.—The purpose of optical instruments is to aid and to extend the powers of the eye. Hence instruments are designed with regard to the properties of the eye, and to understand their action some of the fundamental facts pertaining to the eye and to vision must be known. Actually, the eye is a very complicated instrument, but with regard to its purely optical properties it is essentially like a camera, in that a lens and diaphragm system projects an image on a sensitive screen in a chamber behind them.

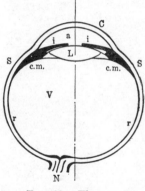

FIG. 68.—The eye.

The structure of the human eye is indicated in Fig. 68. The outer skin, or *sclerotica*, S, contains a transparent window, called the *cornea*, c, directly back of which is the *iris* diaphragm i and *lens L*. In general, whenever light passes through a surface separating two media, the directions of the light rays are changed. Thus when the light rays from external objects pass through the curved surfaces of the cornea and the lens, they are refracted to a focus, which, for clear vision, will be on the inner walls of the eyeball. The greatest part of the refraction occurs at the cornea; in fact, imperfections in focusing such as astigmatism, are usually due to an imperfect corneal curvature. The function of the lens is to supplement the corneal refraction in such a way as to permit accommodation of the eye for objects at various distances. The necessary changes in focus are brought about by changes in the radius of curvature of the front surface of the lens. This is caused by the muscles which hold the lens in place and is more or less automatic. If the accommodation range is abnormal, an

90

external (spectacle) lens may be used to supplement the lens of the eye. In the case of nearsight or myopia, a diverging lens is used; while to correct for the opposite defect, hyperopia, a converging lens is applied.

The inner surface of the sclerotica is covered by a thin black layer, called the *choroidea*. This is covered by the sensitive *retina*. The retina is made up of about forty million nerve endings, which transform the light energy into nerve currents which are transmitted to the brain along the optic nerve. The structure of the retina is indicated in Fig. 69, the light passage being downward. The two kinds of receptors are shown, these being called *rods* or *cones* in accordance with their appearance. Each cone has an individual nerve circuit to the brain, but the rods are connected in groups. The circuits are partly broken at certain places by treelike gaps, or synapses, through which the nerve impulses must pass. These impulses are probably electrical, although they do not travel so rapidly as would be expected.

In one small region of the retina, called the *macula*, there are only cones, and these cones are packed very closely together.

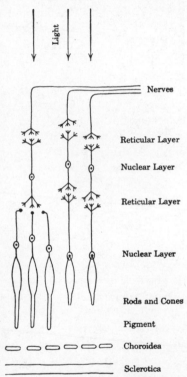

FIG. 69.—A section through the retina.

An image focused on this part of the retina can be analyzed most minutely. When the eyes are turned to look directly at any object, the image is being projected on the macula. The line of sight passes through the center of the macula, which is called the *fovea*. This line makes a slight angle with the optic axis, namely, the line through the centers of curvature of the refracting surfaces. When two points of an object are so close together that they subtend an angle of less than 2 minutes of arc, they will be seen as one, because their images will lie on the same cone. The revelation of new, and often unsuspected, details on objects by the aid of optical instruments is due to their power to increase the angle between pencils of rays which enter the eye from two adjacent points on the object.

⁎ Regions of the retina farther from the fovea contain fewer and fewer cones until in the peripheral regions there are only rods. These are not only farther apart but also connected in groups, so that, while sensitive to the detection of light, this part of the retina is not efficient in resolving details of structure, as everyone knows. The function of the outer retina is to make one aware of the presence of objects, while the macula is for their closer scrutiny. The same economy will be found to exist in the case of color perception.

There are no rods or cones at the point where the optic nerve enters the eye. Hence this spot is blind. This can be easily demonstrated by placing two coins on a table about four inches apart and looking directly with the right eye at the left coin or *vice versa*. If one is at the proper distance, about one foot, the image of the second coin will fall on the optic nerve and it will not be perceived. With a pencil one may map out the form of the blind spot. A diseased retina may have other blind spots which may be located in a similar manner.

The stimulation of the light sensation is not proportional to the intensity of the light. For example, the illumination outdoors in bright sunlight is 6,000 foot-candles, while in a well-lighted room, the illumination may be as low as 3 foot-candles. To an observer, the artificial illumination does not appear to be such a small fraction of that outdoors. This is, however, appreciated by anyone with experience in photography. The visual sensation of brightness is a wholly unreliable index of the actual intensity. This is due to the variation in sensitivity of the eye which automatically takes place when the illumination changes. This is partly accomplished by changes in the size of the iris, but mostly by the secretion of pigment in the eye. This pigment migrates from the choroidea up around the rods and cones and shields them from excessive illumination. When the illumination diminishes, the pigment is gradually reabsorbed. This "dark adaptation" requires about half an hour for its completion. After this time the eye is fully a thousand times as sensitive as it was before.

The intensity of the light sensation also depends on the wave length of the light. This is illustrated by the curves in Fig. 70. The ordinates are the light sensations (brightness) per unit light energy. The curve A refers to ordinary light intensities, while

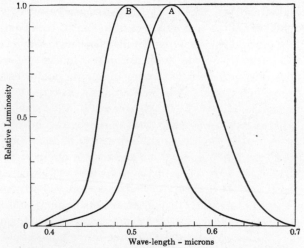

Fig. 70.—Wave-length sensitivity of the human eye.

curve B is for a completely "dark-adapted eye." The maximum ordinates have been arbitrarily set at 1.0, to show the change in shape of the curve more clearly. The shift in sensitivity toward the blue in darkness adaptation is known as the *Purkinje effect*.

Under ordinary conditions a yellow-green light of wave length 0.000055 cm. is the most efficient in stimulating the sensation of light. That is to say, it takes less energy of this wave length to produce a given sensation of brightness than if any other wave length were used. The exact relation is 0.0015 watt per lumen, and this is called the *mechanical equivalent* of light. Outside the range of visible wave lengths, the mechanical equivalent of light is infinite.

78. Vision.—It is important that the sensation of vision aroused by any image does not vanish instantly after cutting off the light but persists for about $\frac{1}{10}$ second. This property is sometimes made use of, notably in moving pictures and in television where successive pictures are seen at a rate of about fifteen per second. The pictures seem to fuse into each other and thus produce the illusion of motion. In the case of television, the neon glow lamp, which replaces the loud speaker on the receiving set, fluctuates in accordance with the brightness of the various parts of the picture or scene which is being scanned by the transmitting apparatus. The broad luminous surface of this lamp is not viewed as a whole, but through a "scanning disc" with a spiral arrangement of holes as shown in Fig. 71. One hole at a time moves across the lamp, each hole crossing a little lower than the preceding, until the end of the spiral is reached at which there is a jump to the top of the picture.

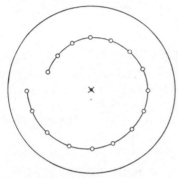

The disc revolves at about fifteen revolutions per second so that the eye receives 15 complete pictures per second. Persistence of vision causes one to see a non-flickering moving picture, whereas

Fig. 71.—"Scanning Disc" for television.

really at any instant one is looking at the neon lamp through one of the small holes.

At the transmitting end there is a similar scanning disc on which an image of the picture or scene is projected. Behind this disc is a photoelectric cell (Art. 142) which translates the varying light intensity falling on it into a fluctuating current. This current is amplified and transmitted to the neon lamp in the same way as the microphone currents are transmitted in telephony or in radiocasting. To obtain undistorted picture reception, the scanning disc on the receiving set must be revolving at the same rate and with the same phase as the disc on the transmitter.

The advantage of having two eyes instead of only one is not only that the image impression is more intense but also that distances are sensed. All objects are seen from a slightly different viewpoint by each eye, and the combination of these two images gives the impression of distance. This is proved by the stereo-scope which consists of a pair of prismatic lenses arranged so that one sees with each eye one of two pictures which were taken from a slightly different viewpoint. Although the pictures are flat, one can see depth when the images projected on the retina differ in the proper way. Microscopes and telescopes are often made in the binocular form to obtain the stereoscopic effect.

79. Accommodation.—Whereas a camera is focused by chang-ing the distance between the lens and screen, the eye is focused by a change in the focal length of the lens itself. This is brought about by the ciliary muscles (*c.m.*), which by their contraction are able to change the curvature of the lens. This is called *accommodation*.

Normally, the eye is accommodated for distant objects. This can be verified by closing them until relaxed and then opening them. Distant objects will be found in focus immediately, while to see close objects clearly a little time is required. A normal eye can see distant objects clearly when relaxed and can accommodate for objects as close as 25 centimeters without undue eyestrain. Since objects subtend the greatest angle at the closest distance, 25 centimeters is called the distance of most distinct vision. It is at this distance that the naked eye can see the most detail.

80. Defective Accommodation.—Often a person's eyes cannot accommodate objects in the range of 25 centimeters to infinity. These two distances are, respectively, called the *near* and the *far* points of the normal eye. Some eyes are nearsighted; *i.e.*, they cannot see distant objects clearly. Their far point is nearer than infinity and their near point is closer than 25 centimeters. Such an eye is said to be *myopic*. It possesses too great a power of convergence. The nearly parallel rays from distant objects are converged too strongly so that the rays come to a focus in front of the retina even when the eye is relaxed (Fig. 72). A ray bundle which comes from nearer objects can, however, be focused on the retina. In the case of distant objects, a properly diverging bundle can be got by the use of a

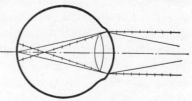

FIG. 72.—Myopia.

diverging lens in front of the eye. Hence myopia can be counteracted by a suitable diverging lens. To find the strength of lens needed, the problem will be considered as a lens-and-image problem. The diverging lens must produce virtual images of objects in front of it such that these images lie in the range of vision for that eye. This must necessarily follow, for the eye itself is not altered, it is still nearsighted; the lens in front of it merely makes the rays seem to come to the eye from points which the unaided eye can accommodate. If the eye is otherwise normal, a diverging lens which will form images of distant objects at the far point of the eye will be the proper lens to use. This lens may not cause the near point to be shifted to a convenient distance. In such a case, separate reading glasses or bifocals must be used.

For the opposite defect, that of a farsighted or so-called *hyperopic* eye, the general principle is the same. Since such an eye does not converge rays strongly enough, a converging lens is necessary to correct it. The lens usually is of such a strength that when the eye is relaxed, the lens and eye combination will focus distant objects sharply on the retina.

If the curvature of the lens or cornea is not the same in all directions, the refracted wave will not be spherical. The eye is then said to be *astigmatic*. To correct for this, a cylindrical lens of the proper strength and orientation is used to compensate for the distortion of the refracting surfaces of the eye. The usual cause of ocular astigmatism is a non-spherical cornea.

81. Simple Microscope.—The apparent size of an object seen by the eye is not so much dependent on the actual size of the object as on the angle it subtends at the eye. The closer an object is placed to the eye, the greater the angle and the larger it appears. It is, however, impossible for the normal eye to see comfortably for any length of time objects closer than 25 centimeters. Nevertheless, it is possible to look through a pinhole at objects like fine print at distances as close as 2 centimeters from the eye. The angle subtended by them is then greater and they appear magnified in the same proportion. Pinhole images are always very faint; so it is customary to use a lens to aid the eye in focusing the rays. A converging lens will aid the eye in accommodating for close objects just as it does in case of farsightedness.

The magnification is the same as that produced by a pinhole with the object at the same distance, but the image is very much brighter. Figure 73 shows a magnifying lens and the virtual image it forms at a distance d which may be 25 (or more) centimeters from the eye. This places the image at a point where it can be seen by a normal eye at least. The object itself is at some distance S from the lens which is slightly less than the focal length f. To calculate the magnification conveniently, it will be assumed that the eye is very close to the lens so that the angles

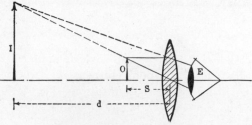

FIG. 73.—The magnifying glass.

subtended at the lens and at the eye are practically the same. Then if O is a small object or a small portion of a larger one, and if I is its image and if β is the angle subtended by them at the eye, then, since for small angles $\beta = \tan \beta$, we can write:

$$\beta = \frac{O}{S}.$$

The largest angle that the object can subtend and still be seen clearly without the lens is the angle subtended by O at a distance of 25 centimeters. Denoting this angle by α, we have

$$\alpha = \frac{O}{25}.$$

Since the retinal image depends on the angle subtended at the eye, the visual magnification obtained when the lens is used is

$$M = \frac{\beta}{\alpha} = \frac{25}{S}.$$

Now S is the object distance corresponding to the virtual image distance $-d$. Therefore

$$\frac{1}{S} = \frac{1}{f} + \frac{1}{d},$$

and

$$M = \frac{25}{f} + \frac{25}{d}.$$

For a normal eye, d may be no smaller than 25 cm; but may be infinitely large, depending on how one focuses the magnifying glass. In the former case ($d = 25$)

$$M = \frac{25}{f} + 1,$$

and in the latter ($d = \infty$)

$$M = \frac{25}{f}.$$

When f is much less than 25 cm., there is no appreciable difference between the two results which represent the two extreme cases. Hence the resulting visual magnification which refers to retinal images is nearly independent of the image distance. This visual magnification may be vastly different from the linear magnification I/O. It tells how much larger an object looks with the aid of optical appliance, which is a matter of angles subtended and not actual sizes alone.

It is seen that the magnification is inversely proportional to the focal length of the lens. This is one reason why $1/f$ has been called the power of a lens.

The formula obtained indicates that any magnifying power may be obtained by merely choosing a lens with a short enough focal length. Although this is true, it is impossible to use a single lens for magnifications above about eight times because of the defects of the image. The utilization of higher magnifications is mainly a problem in designing a combination of lenses in which the defects of the individual lenses will neutralize each other.

82. Eyepieces.—Eyepieces of optical instruments are forms of magnifying glasses of considerable importance. These consist of a combination of lenses at the eye end of the instrument and are used to magnify the image produced by the objective lens. Usually they consist of two lenses mounted a few centimeters apart. A combination of lenses is used instead of one lens, for the purpose of reducing spherical and chromatic aberration.

The lens nearest the eye is called the *eye lens*, and that at the other end is called the *field lens*. The purpose of the latter is to bend the cones of rays coming from the objective so that they focus closer to the axis where more of them may send light to the eye and thus increase the field of view. The two lenses are so shaped and spaced that the light passage through them is as symmetrical as possible. This reduces spherical aberration. The lenses are, moreover, placed exactly or nearly at a distance from each other equal to half the sum of their focal lengths, so that chromatic aberration is nearly eliminated.

The form of eyepiece in common use on microscopes is one designed by Huyghens and shown in Fig. 74*A*. This consists of two plano-convex lenses of which the first has three times the focal length of the second and is placed at a distance of twice the focal length of the second to reduce chromatic aberration. The field lens in combination with the objective produces a real image inside the eyepiece itself. This image is examined by the eye through the eye lens, which produces a virtual image in a position convenient for visual examination.

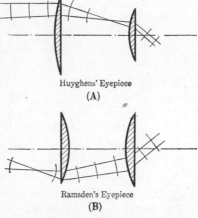

Huyghens' Eyepiece
(A)

Ramsden's Eyepiece
(B)

Fig. 74.—Eyepieces.

If cross-wires or a scale are to be used in the instrument, another form of eyepiece is preferable. This is known as the Ramsden eyepiece (Fig. 74*B*). It can be focused on an image in front of the entire combination instead of only between its component parts. Cross-wires or a scale may then be fixed in the tube in front of the eyepiece and the image projected on them. The eyepiece as a whole magnifies both the image and the scale or the wires. Such an arrangement is much easier to focus besides possessing the advantage of a less distorted image on the cross-wires. The field lens of the Huyghens combination does not bend all the cones of rays toward the axis in quite the right proportion to make an undistorted image for measurement. The Huyghens combination is, however, more perfectly corrected for spherical and chromatic aberration so that it is used whenever the image is not to be projected on a scale or cross-wires.

The Ramsden eyepiece is made up of two plano-convex lenses of equal focal length separated by a distance equal to three-quarters of the focal length of either lens. The separation is not exactly half the sum of the focal lengths of the two lenses. The reason for this is that if the lenses were so placed, the surface of the field lens would be seen in the eye lens together with all dirt marks or scratches that might be on it, and this would mar the image. The actual construction is a compromise which throws the surface of the first lens out of focus without having a very bad effect on the corrections for the aberrations.

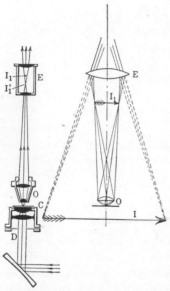

83. Compound Microscope.—A simple plano-convex lens will magnify up to eight times without the aberrations being too harmful. From magnifications up to about twenty, however, combinations of lenses such as the Ramsden eyepiece just described are very suitable. For magnifications of several hundred, a still more complicated combination of lenses must be employed in order that the necessary corrections may be made for the various aberrations and so produce a bright image showing the finest detail clearly. Such a combination of lenses is called a compound microscope. A cross-section of one showing the lens system is given in Fig. 75, together with a simplified two-lens system which illustrates the most essential optical processes. The lens system O, which is called the objective, forms an image I_1 of the object which is again magnified by the eyepiece E. A Huyghens eyepiece is usually employed, the image falling beyond

Fig. 75.—Compound microscope.

OPTICAL INSTRUMENTS 101

the field lens and being displaced by it to I_1'. This does not change the simple theory of magnification, as illustrated in the diagram, for the first image, I_1 may be considered to be magnified by the combination of lenses which make up the eyepiece as by a single unit. The magnification by the eyepiece alone will be $M_e = 25/f_2$ as before, and that for the objective will be $M_o = L/f_1$, where L is approximately the length of the microscope tube, 25 is the distance of most distinct vision, from which the object would be examined without a microscope, and f_1 and f_2 are, respectively, the focal lengths of the objective and of the eyepiece. The resultant magnification will be

$$M = \frac{25L}{f_1 f_2}.$$

For a high magnification, the formula clearly shows that the focal lengths both of the objective and of the eyepiece should be short and that the length of the tube should be as great as is convenient.

In the chapter on Diffraction it will be explained why the finest detail separately distinguished in any image depends on the wave length of the light used and on the aperture of the cone of rays which enter the objective lens. The distance between two points which are so close as to be just separated in the image is proportional to the wave length of the light used and inversely proportional to the aperture. For a microscope, this leads to the conclusion that it is impossible to make a microscope which will show separately two points closer together than about one-third of the average wave length of the light used.

84. Astronomical Telescope.—An astronomical telescope likewise consists of a pair of lens systems for similar reasons as in the case of a microscope. In this case, however, the object is very far away from the first lens, so that the image is very nearly at its focus instead of the object being near the focus as before. Figure 76 shows a cross-section through a telescope. Usually crosswires and a Ramsden eyepiece are used. Since the object is to be regarded as inaccessible, the telescope brings about a magnification merely by enlarging the visual angle. This angular magnification is usually much larger than the linear magnification of the object. The magnification produced by the objective alone is $M_0 = \beta/\alpha$, where α is the angle subtended by the object (Fig. 76) and β is the angle subtended by I_1, the image by the objective alone, when this is viewed from the distance of most distinct vision. The magnification by the eyepiece is, similarly, γ/β so that the resultant magnification due to both is γ/α, where γ is the angle subtended by I_1 and I from the eyepiece lens. Because

$$\alpha = \frac{I_1}{f_1} \text{ and } \gamma = \frac{I_1}{f_2} \text{ (approximately);}$$

$$M = \frac{\gamma}{\alpha} = \frac{f_1}{f_2}.$$

For high magnifications this shows that the focal length of the objective should be great while that of the eyepiece should be short. For this reason objectives for astronomical telescopes often have focal lengths of 40 to 60 feet. The largest refracting

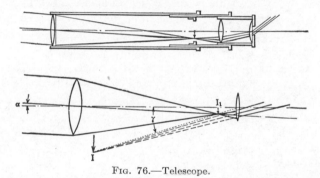

FIG. 76.—Telescope.

telescope in the world is at the Yerkes observatory at Williams Bay, Wisconsin, the objective having a diameter of 40 inches and a focal length of 60 feet.

85. Terrestrial Telescopes.—The fact that the final image is inverted is no inconvenience for some purposes, such as astronomy, but for terrestrial work it is often desirable to have an erect image. This is sometimes produced by an extra set of lenses placed between the objective and the eyepiece. These lenses invert the image but do not change the magnification, as shown in Fig. 77. The addition of these lenses makes the telescope tube still longer, so that more often other schemes are preferred to obtain the same effect.

One of these other arrangements for inverting the image is a set of prisms, as shown in Fig. 78. These allow a long optical path compared with the tube length besides reinverting the image. The two telescopes of the common binoculars are of this type.

Another arrangement is one which employs a diverging lens for the eyepiece. The length of the tube is then $f_1 - f_2$ instead

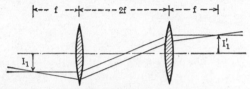

FIG. 77.—Reinversion of image.

of $f_1 + f_2$ as in the ordinary telescope. This is shown in Fig. 79. The first telescopes made by Galileo were of this type. In modern times the idea is very commonly used in the construction of opera glasses.

86. The Camera.— A camera consists of a lens, diaphragm, and shutter, mounted in an opening of an otherwise light-tight box into which the image is projected. The most important part is

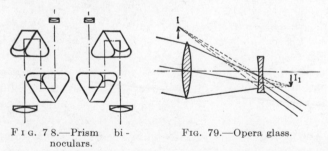

FIG. 78.—Prism binoculars.

FIG. 79.—Opera glass.

the lens which must be highly corrected for a large number of aberrations. Other than those already mentioned, there are curvature of image and distortion. It is also desirable that the opening of the lens be large, so that a large amount of light is used to form the image and thus cut down the time required to obtain an impression on the photographic plate. Often, too, the field of view should be large. These ends are attained, as far as possible, by building up a lens system out of lenses of various shapes and chemical composition. The problem is a very exacting one for the lens designer.

Distortion of image is a serious defect in a photographic lens, especially when architectural pictures are to be made. When a plano-convex lens is placed with the flat side facing the object, the greater refraction of oblique rays shortens the image, especially in the outer portions. This distorts a square into a barrel-shaped figure. A diaphragm in front of the lens increases the distortion. A diaphragm in this position allows passage only of the rays which are the most in error. If the lens is turned around, the opposite effect is produced, and this is increased by a diaphragm

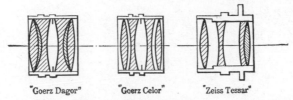

"Goerz Dagor"   "Goerz Celor"   "Zeiss Tessar"

Fig. 80.—Photographic lenses.

behind the lens. Since the type of distortion depends on the direction of light through the lens, it is possible to combine two exactly similar lenses symmetrically on the two sides of a diaphragm and thus eliminate the distortion. Such a combination is called a rectilinear lens or an orthoscopic doublet.

A good photographic lens corrected for all important aberrations consists of at least four individual lenses and often six. Figure 80 shows cross-sections of some of the typical high-grade lenses.

The function of the diaphragm is to permit changes in the intensity of the image, and to allow variation of the depth of focus. Both of these effects depend on the size of the cone of rays transmitted through the lens. With the diaphragm wide open, the cone of rays is large, the image is bright, and the plate must be placed at or near the exact focus in order that the image appear sharp. In this connection it must be recalled that the eye does not distinguish detail finer than is subtended by an angle of 2 minutes. Hence a spot of light need only subtend 2 minutes of arc in order that it appear as a point to the naked eye. As Fig.

81 shows, this gives a certain range AB in which the plate may be placed and still depict a sharp image. The figure shows clearly why a narrow cone of rays will allow a greater latitude of focus. Not only is there no need to have the plate exactly at the focus, for one image, but images of other objects, near and far, will also not appear to be much out of focus.

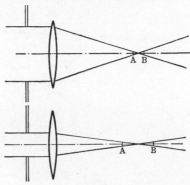

FIG. 81.—Depth of focus.

The intensity of the image is directly proportional to the area of the lens opening and inversely proportional to the square of the distance to the image. Thus

$$I \propto \frac{d^2}{f^2},$$

where d is the diameter of the opening. The ratio of f to d is called the f-value of the opening. The common diaphragm numbers in the first column of Table V mean that the diameters of the openings are, respectively, the fractions of the focal length given in the second column. These fractions are such that their squares, which are proportional to the brightness of the image, decrease by factors of one-half. Since the brightness is inversely proportional to the exposure required, the relative exposures are as given in the third column. These numbers are often called the U. S. values of the diaphragm openings.

87. Projection Lantern.—Optically, the projection lantern is like the photographic camera, in that a lens is used to produce a real image on a screen. In this case, however, the relative positions of object and image are reversed. The object is a transparent slide illuminated from behind by an arc lamp or other source with a set of condensing lenses. These lenses increase both the illumination and the field of view. Without a condenser, the light from the outer portions of the slide would not pass through the projecting lens unless it were as large as the

TABLE V

f-value of stop	Fraction of f	U. S. value of stop
4	$\frac{1}{4}$	1
5.7	$\frac{1}{5.7}$	2
8	$\frac{1}{8}$	4
11	$\frac{1}{11}$	8
16	$\frac{1}{16}$	16
22	$\frac{1}{22}$	32
32	$\frac{1}{32}$	64

lantern slide. Large lenses of the quality needed for projection would be too costly. The condenser overcomes this difficulty and enlarges the field of view by directing all cones of rays toward the objective from even the edges of the slide, so that a small projection lens is sufficient. The projection lens is usually of

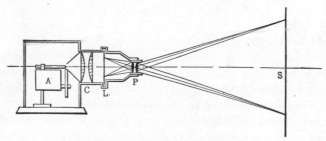

FIG. 82.—Projection lantern.

the photographic type. Figure 82 illustrates the action of the condensing and projecting lenses.

88. Spectroscopes.—It has been shown that a prism resolves light into a spectrum which indicates the wave lengths radiated by the source. A pure spectrum is obtained only with a narrow slit and a set of lenses which produce sharp images of the slit. An instrument for the purpose of observing spectra is called a *spectroscope*. The optical arrangement is often as shown in Fig. 83. A slit and lens at the ends of tube *C* make up the part called the *collimator* which renders the light falling on the prism parallel. The refracted light is received by the telescope *T* which is focused for parallel rays, so that a real image of the spectrum is thrown on the cross-wires *w* and then magnified by the eyepiece *E*. Parallel light is used in the refraction because this light remains parallel and hence stays focused during any

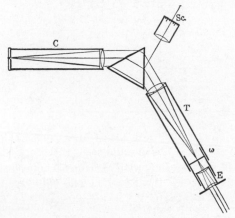

FIG. 83.—Spectroscope.

rotation or change in position of the prism. Often a scale of wave-lengths *S* is reflected into the telescope so that its image coincides with that of the spectrum. If the scale is properly made, it will be possible to read off wave lengths directly when it has been adjusted for any known spectrum line.

Sometimes the tubes are fixed and the wave lengths read off a micrometer screw which causes small rotations of the prism. In this connection a quadrilateral prism of special construction is used in some commercial wave-length spectroscopes. Such instruments are often used to approximately determine wave lengths of light.

If the prism is mounted on a divided circle and the telescope attached to verniers which rotate around it, the instrument is called a *spectrometer*. It is then suitable for measuring angles of deviation and angles of prisms. With the prism in minimum deviation the angle A of the prism and D of deviation can be measured and the index of refraction found by a formula given in the chapter on Refraction.

If a camera is used instead of a telescope the instrument is called a *spectrograph*. The construction of individual instruments may vary but the underlying principles are the same.

Problems

1. A nearsighted eye cannot see clearly beyond 5 m. What is the power of a lens which will enable it to see distant objects clearly? *Ans.* $-0.2D$.

2. A farsighted eye cannot see objects clearly when they are nearer than 1 m. What lens will enable it to read a book 25 cm. away? *Ans.* $+3.0D$.

3. The focal lengths of two lenses are, respectively, 10 and 65 cm. What telescopic arrangement will give the greatest magnification and what will it be? *Ans.* $F_o = 65$; $F_e = 10$; $M = 6.5$.

4. What is the linear magnification of the telescope of Problem 3, if the object is 5,000 m. away, and the final image is 25 cm. from the eye? *Ans.* M (lin.) $= 0.000455$.

5. A telescope objective has a focal length of 50 cm. How much motion must be allowed the eyepiece if it is to be used for objects as close as 2 m. as well as objects very distant? *Ans.* 16.67 cm.

6. The eyepiece of a telescope has to be moved 1 cm. to focus an object 25 cm. away, having been originally focused for a distant object. What is the focal length of the telescope objective? *Ans.* $+4.5$ cm.

7. A microscope is to be adjusted to magnify one thousand times. The eyepiece chosen has a focal length of 1.5 cm. and the tube length is 20 cm.; what must be the focal length of the objective? *Ans.* ⅓ cm.

8. An opera glass is to be constructed having a magnification of 4 and a tube length of 6 cm. What must be the focal lengths of the lenses? *Ans.* $F_o = 8$ cm.; $F_e = -2$ cm.

9. A camera lens has a focal length of 6.5 in. The limit of the bellows draw is 8 in. What is the maximum magnification obtainable and how far must the object be placed from the lens? *Ans.* $M = 0.23$; $u = 34.67$ in.

10. With a lamp 15 cm. from an object an exposure of 1 sec. is needed. What exposure is needed if the lamp is moved to 45 cm. from the object and the diaphragm is changed from $f8$ to $f32$? *Ans.* 144 sec.

11. The radius of the cornea is 7.83 mm. and the index of refraction of the aqueous humour is 1.3365; what is the equivalent power in diopters of the corneal refraction? *Ans.* $+43.0$ diopters.

12. The index of refraction of the lens of the eye is 1.430 and that of the aqueous and vitreous humours is 1.336; the radii of curvature of the lens faces are 10 and 6 mm. What is the power of the lens in diopters? *Ans.* $+18.7$ diopters.

13. A camera lens has a focal length of 20 cm. and the distance to the film is 30 cm. What is the focal length of the lens which must be combined with the camera lens in order to obtain a magnification of two times? *Ans.* +20 cm.

14. If the near and far points of an unaided eye are, respectively, at 0.2 and 1 m., what will be the range of clear vision with a −1.0 diopter spectacle lens? *Ans.* 25 cm. to ∞.

CHAPTER IX

COLOR

89. Production of Color.—Sensations of color play an important part in vision. The physical reality which determines the visual quality of the radiation is the intensity distribution in the visible spectrum. This is perceived by means of the human eye as color. The eye, however, sees intensity distributions imperfectly and in a very qualitative manner. Thus there may be an infinite number of physically different radiations which excite the same color sensation. A complete analysis of the quality of light can be obtained only by means of intensity measurements within the spectrum of the radiation. This is accomplished with the aid of an instrument called the spectrophotometer. Qualitative analyses may be made with the use of a spectroscope. Conclusions reached by eye alone may be very misleading.

Starting with a beam of light which appears white, one often finds that after some reflection, refraction, or other optical process, the light becomes colored. Processes in which changes of this kind take place are said to be *selective*, since a spectroscopic examination shows that all wave lengths have not been affected in the same degree. Several such selective effects observed with interference will be considered in the following chapters. This chapter will deal chiefly with the results of selective absorption and contains a brief discussion of selective scattering which causes the colors seen in the sky.

Since the sky is not black, it must send some light to the eye. This must involve the deviation of some of the light coming from the sun. It is brought about by reflection and diffraction of light by minute particles of dust or water vapor which are small enough to float in the air without settling. Even the air molecules contribute to the effect. Such tiny particles will naturally scatter aside the shorter waves while the long waves

110

will pass over them more readily. Hence the scattered light contains an excess of blue while the transmitted light contains an excess of red. The red will be especially prominent when the sunlight passes through a long distance of air as during sunrise and sunset. The reds are increased in brilliance by the addition of fine particles to the air, as when there are big forest fires or volcanic eruptions. This increases the number of scattering particles and makes the transmitted beam more highly colored. Large particles do not have a selective effect. They cause the different shades of gray seen in clouds.

90. Selective Absorption.—The most common origin of color in the objects seen about us lies in the selective absorption of dye compounds. If the colored light is analyzed prismatically, it will be observed that the light which is diffusely reflected from the surface of the colored material has had the intensity of some of its constituent wave lengths diminished to a greater extent than others. Since these colors are the same in transmitted as in reflected light, it appears that the latter must have passed through some of the surface irregularities so as to be selectively absorbed. The fact that if the surface is polished, the direct reflection off the top is not colored, is a confirmation of this. There is always some white light off the surface mixed with the color due to selective absorption. The color is said to be unsaturated because it differs from pure spectral colors by containing an admixture of white light. This may also take place because of the imperfect selectiveness of ordinary dyes. The surface reflection, however, is often a big factor as can be shown by powdering the substance and thus increasing the surface. Many colored crystals or colored glasses, or even clear glass, are white when finely powdered.

The surface reflections are not always white. Some substances, such as gold, or blocks of some aniline dyes, have a true selective surface reflection. Even in finely powdered form they reflect the same light as a single sheet. Moreover, the light transmitted by thin sheets is complementary to that reflected. For example, thin gold leaf transmits blue-green light, thus showing that yellow has been selectively reflected at the surface.

In most cases, however, there is no selective surface reflection and the color is due to the light which penetrates into the substance.   The color or hue of such an object depends on more than just the type of absorption.   It also depends on the quality of the light which falls on it.   Everyone knows how differently a colored object appears in artificial light and in daylight.   Colors which match in one light may appear entirely different in another. It is instructive to exaggerate this condition and observe colored objects in brightly colored lights or in white and mercury lights. It will be found that one may, for example, match orange and yellow papers in red light since they both have the same effect on that part of the spectrum, but that in other colors the match will appear absurd.   The changed appearance of reddish objects in mercury light is very striking.   This is due to the fact that the mercury arc radiates very little red light.

In a pure spectral color of a single wave length, all non-luminous objects have the same hue.   They can reflect no other wave length than the one falling on them.   Hence, objects in such light will appear merely lighter or darker depending on their absorbing power for that wave length.   Instruments for the measurement of absorbing and reflecting powers for different wave lengths are called *spectrophotometers*.

91. Colorimetry.—Each color is usually defined by its hue, its saturation, and its brightness.   This is the basis of monochromatic colorimetry and also the ordinary designation of colors. One says, for example, that a color is blue, thus designating its hue, and that it is a pale blue, telling roughly that it contains an admixture of white, and that it is bright or faint according to its intensity.   An instrument for scientifically determining these factors is called a colorimeter.   It consists of a photometer containing a divided field attached to a spectroscope.   One half of the field is illuminated directly by the light to be tested while the other half is illuminated by a spectral color, the wave length of which can be varied, and to which an adjustable amount of white light can be added.   One obtains an intensity and color match of the two halves of the field and reads off hue in terms of wave length of the spectral color used, the saturation in per cent of white that had to be added and the intensity in terms of some standard intensity.   In the case of reflecting surfaces, the brightness specification is given in percentage reflection because the actual brightness depends on that of the light used.   All colors can be analyzed by this method except purples, because these are mixtures of the two ends of the spectrum. They are measured by the color and intensity that must be added to produce white light, *i.e.*, by finding their complementary.

This method of color analysis does not tell enough about the physical nature of the color, that is, if it is pure or a combination, and, therefore if colors are mixed, the results are sometimes unexpected. More information is needed about the colored light and about color mixture in order to understand these effects.

92. Additive and Subtractive Color Mixture.—There are two methods of color mixture that can well be illustrated by the use of complementary blue and yellow solutions. These may be made by dissolving copper sulphate and ferric chloride, respectively, in water. If on the screen a blue beam and a separate yellow beam are projected, the portions where they overlap will be white. The colors are therefore complementary, since this is what is meant by the term. The process of combining colored beams in this way is called additive color combination. The tendency in this process is always to produce more light and to approach white.

On the other hand, if one beam passes through both solutions, the resultant color will be green. This is called subtractive color mixture and the tendency in such cases is to obtain less light and to approach black.

These effects are readily explained by a more comprehensive analysis of the colored beams. The most thorough analysis of the light that can be made is a spectral resolution into the pure spectral colors and a measurement of the intensity of each. This process is called *spectrophotometry*. Examples of such analyses of the light transmitted by five dyes are given in Fig. 84.

The two methods of color mixing may be illustrated and explained by means of such spectrophotometric curves as these. Consider the yellow and blue beams. If they are combined as in the additive process, the result is the sum of the intensities as shown in Fig. 85*A*. The two beams supplement each other and tend toward white. If, however, the two dyes are mixed as in the subtractive process, an effect depending on the combined transmission factor of the mixture for each wave length is

obtained.   This is found by multiplying the transmission factors
of the two dyes at every wave length.   The wave-length region of
best transmission for the combination is that region which both

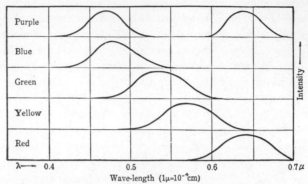

Fig. 84.—Spectrophotometric curves.

transmit well, for if either one has a low transmission for any
wave, the value for the mixture will also be low.   In Fig. 85*B* are
shown the spectrophotometric curves for the subtractive process.
The two colors add together to produce less light than before.

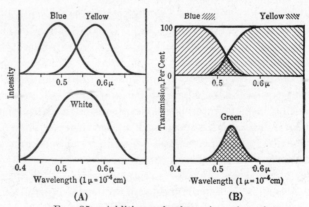

Fig. 85.—Additive and subtractive color mixture.

93. Primary Colors.—It is found that the visual sensations are
of such a nature that all colors as well as white can be produced
by combining only three colors.   These three are called *primary
colors.*   For the additive process they are red, green, and violet.

The violet used is a true violet, not purple, and is sometimes called deep blue. Red and green give yellow and all the intermediate shades; green and violet give a greenish blue; and violet and red give purple. All hues can be produced by using the right proportions of these primaries. For subtractive combination there are also three primaries but these are just the complementaries of the above. They are greenish blue, magenta, and yellow. These are approximately the blue, red, and yellow which are used in painting.

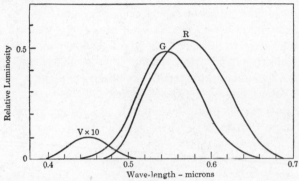

FIG. 86.—The three primary color sensations stimulated by light of various wave length.

The analysis of colored lights into the constituent additive primaries is called trichromatic colorimetry. This method is better than the monochromatic from the standpoint of color mixture but it is not so natural, for it omits hue, saturation and brightness. These may, however, be calculated from the analysis.

94. Color Vision.—The eye is such a poor judge of the spectral composition of light, that all color sensations can be excited by the combination of only three primary colors, namely, red, green, and violet. Because of this fact, Young and Helmholtz suggested that the sensation of light is made up of a combination of three color sensations which correspond to the red, green, and violet primaries in additive color mixture. Each spectral colored light stimulates the three primary colors in characteristic proportions. Koenig found the relative stimulation of the three primaries by the various wave lengths in the spectrum of white light. His results are illustrated in Fig. 86. The sum of the three curves gives the curve *A* in Fig. 70 which refers to the total light sensation.

Sometimes one of the three color senses is lacking and the individual is then color-blind. Usually it is the red sensation, sometimes the green, and very rarely the violet that is missing. About 4 per cent of men and about one-fourth of 1 per cent of women are color-blind. Usually the person himself is not aware of color-blindness. It requires some kind of test, such as matching colored yarns or projected patches of light, to show that the color sense is defective. It is essential that the objects be such that the individual has not associated some color name with them. A striking error that the red blind are likely to make is to match green with orange, or deep red with brown or dark gray.

Trichromatic color vision of the type discussed above exists only in the macula and for lights of ordinary intensity. In other words, it refers only to the cone vision. Around the macula is a zone of partial color-blindness in the case of even normal eyes. In this zone orange and green are confused very much as in the case of red blindness. The vision is here dichromatic, the primary colors being yellow and blue. Still farther from the macula the retina is entirely color-blind. These zones can be mapped out by fixing the eye at some definite point and having some one bring in colored objects from the side and noting how far toward the center they must be before the colors can be distinguished without error. At very low intensities, the entire eye is color-blind. This occurs near the threshold of vision and is associated with the Purkinje effect. Under these conditions one sees only with the rods.

There are several other theories of color vision of which the best is the theory proposed by Hering. Considering all phases of the problem, the physical and physiological, as well as the psychological, these other theories have no advantage over the modern form of trichromatic theory. The latter is still referred to as the Young-Helmholtz theory in honor of the pioneers in this field, although it has no longer the simple form which they gave it.

95. Color Printing.—The printing of pictures in color is an application of color mixture. Three plates are prepared, each of which will print a picture giving the proper relative intensities of one of the subtractive primaries. These are printed over each other to give the picture in natural colors. The subtractive primaries, magenta, yellow, and blue must be used. The first is white minus green, the second is minus violet, and the last is minus red. In other words, the first absorbs only green, the second only violet, and the third only red. Mixtures of them can be made which will take out the desired amounts of the real primaries and so give any color. Thus a combination of magenta and yellow subtracts green and violet and leaves red. A combination of yellow and blue subtracts violet and red and leaves green, while magenta and blue leave only violet. Similar results are obtained in mixing pigments for painting.

96. Color Photography.—Photographs in natural colors can also be made by such a three-color process. Three negatives are made by exposing three panchromatic plates, respectively, behind red, green, and violet color filters. The result is a set of black and white negatives which record the relative amounts of each primary color in the different parts of the picture. These negatives are printed on bichromated gelatin film. When this is developed in warm water, the gelatin washes away where it has not been acted on by the light and this leaves the picture standing out in relief. Each of these films is then placed in its appropriate dye bath which is in each case complementary to the color on the screen through which the picture was made. The dye is absorbed more strongly in the thicker parts of the film. The three films are superposed and attached to each other and to a white background, giving the finished picture in colors. The method is not very easy because one has to get just the right proportion of each color. A simplified modification of this method which employs only two primary colors—reddish orange and bluish green—is often used in the motion pictures. The pictures in the two colors are printed, respectively, on the two sides of the film.

A simpler process and a very ingenious one is that known as the *autochrom*. This process produces the colors by the addition of red, green, and violet beams. A plate of glass is coated with a mixture of very tiny transparent starch granules of which proper amounts have been dyed violet, green, and red. Behind this is a very thin panchromatic emulsion. The picture is exposed in the ordinary way with the starch grain filters toward the oncoming light so that they filter it before it reaches the sensitive film. When the plate is developed the film is blackened behind each of the starch grains in proportion to the prominence of the color which it transmits. If the plate is now held up to the light, it will show the picture in complementary colors. The colors are then reversed by dissolving the blackened silver and then blackening the remainder of the emulsion which was not at first affected by the light. The colors seen in the final picture are produced by this mosaic of tiny starch grains, the particular intensity of each primary color being controlled by the darkness of the silver deposited behind it. This method yields a transparency which must be viewed in transmitted light. To obtain prints of the pictures they must virtually be photographed in color by some subtractive process.

In the new Kodacolor amateur moving picture film, the colors are furnished by a tricolor filter (red, green, and violet) which is placed over the lens. The film has a ribbed surface, the ribs acting as cylindrical lenses. When the pictures are taken, the ribs make strip images of the color filter on the sensitive emulsion and cause a simultaneous record of the three color components of the object being photographed to be produced in narrow adjacent strips on the film. When the pictures are projected, the converse ray passage is obtained, the ribs causing the light from each strip to pass through the appropriate color filter. The colors are then seen by an additive fusion of the primary colors.

Problems

1. What is the hue of a dye which absorbs (a) red, (b) green, (c) violet? *Ans.* (a) Greenish blue; (b) magenta; (c) yellow.

2. If the transmission curves for two colored glasses are known, how can the curve for the two placed together be obtained? *Ans.* By multiplication of the transmissions for each wave length.

3. Explain in a general way (*e.g.*, by formula) how any color can be produced as an additive combination of three primary colors, and as a subtractive combination. *Ans.* Any Color $=$ x per cent red $+$ y per cent green $+$ z per cent violet, or Any Color $=$ white light $-$ a per cent red $-$ b per cent green $-$ c per cent violet.

CHAPTER X

INTERFERENCE

97. General Principles.—When the wave theory of light was introduced in the fourth chapter, an experiment devised by Thomas Young, in 1800, was described which showed that it was possible for two beams of light to "interfere." This can be clearly understood only if light is considered to have the characteristics of a wave motion. It is to be expected that the sum of two waves is dependent on the phases of the vibrations. If these waves arrive at some points in opposite phase there will be minimum intensities at these points, while at other points where the phases are the same there will be maximum effects.

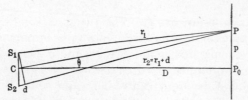

Fig. 87.—Difference in path from two sources.

This will produce the alternate light and dark bands or "fringes" which are characteristic of interference.

The general principles of interference are derived by a consideration of the addition of waves. Suppose that there are two waves arriving simultaneously at a point P (Fig. 87) one of these waves having traveled a distance d farther than the other. If this distance d is any integral multiple of a wave length, the two waves will arrive in phase at P, provided that they started in phase. Under these conditions, there will be brightness at P. At a point such that the one wave travels an integral number of waves plus a half wave farther than the other, the two waves will arrive in opposite phase if they start in phase, and there will be darkness at any such point. Very often the two sources are

119

vibrating in opposite phase, or one of the beams suffers a sudden reversal in phase before it reaches the point P. The first case may be called a sudden reversal in phase of one of the beams right at the source. Whenever there is such a sudden reversal due to any cause, the path difference d does not solely determine the phases of the two vibrations arriving at P. The effect is to make the waves arrive in phase if d is an integral number of waves plus a half, and out of phase if d is an integral number of waves. It will be found that a number of such cases exist. These statements may be summarized as follows: When

$$d = m\lambda \begin{cases} \text{intensity } maxima \text{ occur if there is no sudden phase change} \\ \text{intensity } minima \text{ occur if the phase suddenly reverses} \end{cases}$$

and when

$$\begin{matrix} d = (m + \tfrac{1}{2})\lambda \\ \text{or} \\ d = (2m + 1)\dfrac{\lambda}{2} \end{matrix} \begin{cases} \text{intensity } minima \text{ occur if there is no sudden} \\ \text{phase change} \\ \text{intensity } maxima \text{ occur if the phase suddenly} \\ \text{reverses} \end{cases}$$

where m takes on any integral value: 0, 1, 2, 3, . . .

98. Examples of Interference.—The most important consideration in producing interference is to obtain two sources which are exactly similar down to the smallest electronic vibration. Light from two different sources or even from different points in the same source will not interfere. The reason for this is that the different electrons which radiate the light waves change phases very rapidly, in fact about one-hundred million times per second. Hence, two electrons will change from "in phase" to "out of phase" so fast that the light at the point where the waves come together will appear as a steady average because the eye cannot follow fluctuations of intensity which are faster than about 30 per second. Therefore, no interference bands will be seen. Sources which do not change their relative phases between corresponding points are called *coherent sources*. They are always produced by using one source and making part of the light travel one path while another part travels a different path. Considering Young's experiment, S_1 and S_2 are the two coherent sources, but the light really comes from a single source S (Fig. 17). The experiment will fail if S_1 and S_2 are two independent sources. As it is, if there is any change in phase in one source, and these changes occur with great frequency, there will be exactly the same change in phase in the other and hence no difference in phase between the two. The differences in phase will be determined solely by the path differences to the various parts of the illuminated screen.

In Fig. 17, the single slit S is shown in such a location that the light travels the same distance to S_1 as to S_2. Hence these two sources are in phase and maxima occur at points P for which $d = m\lambda$. Suppose that the slit is moved upward or downward to a point such that the light from S travels a half wave farther to one of the pair of slits. Then S_1 and S_2 are in opposite phase and minima will occur at points such that $d = m\lambda$, that is, at the same points as those at which maxima occurred before. If there are two slits, therefore, instead of one at S, or even a single slit so broad that the midpoints of its two halves are located as in the two cases considered separately above, then the interference bands will vanish and a uniform average illumination will be seen. Hence the slit S in Young's experiment and in some of the experiments to be described, must be narrow to obtain clearly visible interference bands. The method devised by Michelson for the measurement of star diameters depends on this vanishing of the interference bands due to the width of the source. The star is the source S, while S_1 and S_2 are two small mirrors mounted so that the distance between them can be changed. The fringes vanish when the distance between S_1 and S_2 is made such that the fringe systems due to the two halves of the star are complementary and smooth each other out.

Usually the two coherent sources are produced by reflection or refraction of light from a single narrow source. A device invented by Fresnel consists of two mirrors inclined at a slight angle with each other, as shown in Fig. 88. These produce two virtual images very close together and it is this reflected light which interferes in places on the screen. This is a better example of pure interference than Young's experiment, because the beams are united by reflection and not by the non-rectilinear propagation of light. In Young's experiment, the light from S which passes through S_1 and S_2 would not come together at any point P on the screen if it were not for the fact that light does not exactly travel in straight lines. To make use of this effect, the slits S_1 and S_2 must be very narrow and close together. In Fresnel's experiment (Fig. 88), the source S is a slit parallel to the inter-section of the mirrors. The bands are seen in the region of the overlapping beams. The light is virtually coming from the

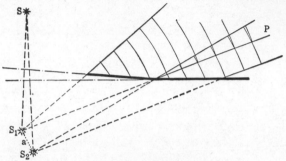

FIG. 88.—Fresnel's mirrors.

images in the mirrors and d is the path difference to any point P. Another device, also due to Fresnel, is the biprism which produces coherent sources by refraction. The prism angle is nearly 180 degrees, so that the images are very close together, as shown in Fig. 89. Still another device is the split lens of Billet. This is a

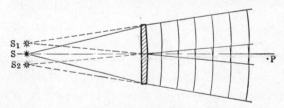

FIG. 89.—Fresnel's biprism.

convex lens cut in two along a diameter so that it produces two images close together. The fringes are seen in the overlapping beams after the light diverges from the images.

The simplest of all is the Lloyd mirror which consists of merely a perfectly plane plate of glass which is preferably black, to cut down internal reflections. At grazing reflection, an image of a slit S is formed close to it as shown in Fig. 90. The direct light from the slit and the light from the image interfere.

In all these cases, virtually the conditions shown in Fig. 87 exist. Two coherent sources are a distance a apart and a distance D from the screen on which the bands are to be observed. To find the path difference d of the two waves, draw an arc

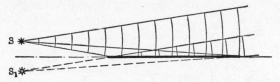

FIG. 90.—Lloyd's mirror.

through S_1 with P as a center. The value of d is derived as in Art. **28,** and it is found that

$$d = a \sin \theta.$$

Since the angle θ is usually a fraction of a degree, its sine can be replaced by its tangent which is p/D where p denotes the distance of P from P_0. Therefore $d = ap/D$. Substituting this result for d in the fundamental equations for interference it is found that: when

$$ap/D = m\lambda \qquad \text{or} \qquad p = m(D\lambda/a),$$

intensity maxima occur, and when

$$ap/D = (m + \tfrac{1}{2})\lambda \text{ or } p = (m + \tfrac{1}{2})(D\lambda/a),$$

intensity minima occur. As m is given all successive integral values, it is seen that a set of equally spaced alternate bright and dark bands appears on the screen. The spacing of the bright or of the dark bands is $D\lambda/a$ (see Fig. 18).

99. Newton's Rings.—Thin films of transparent material like soap bubbles, or oil on water, show brilliant colors. The origin of the colors was studied by Newton who devised a simple and effective means for securing a film of air of varying thickness. For this purpose he used a convex lens of a large radius R which was pressed against a plane plate of glass, as shown in Fig. 91. The thickness of the film a varies with the distance from the point of contact and is easily calculated at any point by the sagitta formula.

$$a = \frac{y^2}{2R},$$

where y is the distance from the center. The loci of points of equal thickness are evidently circles of radius y around the point of contact. The interference bands are therefore circular as shown in Fig. 92.

When white light is used, the rings are colored in both reflected and transmitted light, the colors in the two systems being com-

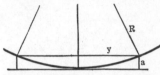

FIG. 91 —Thickness of film between sphere and plane.

plementary at corresponding points. It is as though the reflection coefficient of the film for any color varied with the thickness of the film, the color not reflected being transmitted. Newton found it very difficult to explain this apparent selective reflection on the corpuscular theory.

100. Explanation of Newton's Rings.—The formation of Newton's rings is easily explained on the basis of interference.　Con-

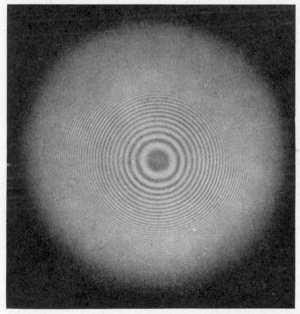

FIG. 92.—A photograph of Newton's rings.

sider a portion of a Newton's air film $LMNO$ highly magnified (Fig. 93).　A ray S incident on the film as shown will be reflected back and forth inside the film with some of the light escaping at each reflection. These rays will get weaker with each reflection, so that only the first two or three are of much importance. The reflected rays will cross at some point P_1 above the film if it gets thinner to the right, and below it if thinner to the left (virtual). The interference effects are localized at such points. For any single wave length, a dark band will occur wherever the thickness of the film is such that the relative retardation of the rays from the top and bottom surface is an odd multiple of a half wave. These bands will be contour lines of equal thickness of the film; hence circles in the case of a lens pressed against a plate. The lenses L_1 and L_2 may be used to project their images on a screen. In case of direct observation, the lens of the eye projects their images directly on the retina. The fringes are most distinct for perpendicular incidence and for thicknesses of film between 0.00016 and 0.0008 millimeter.

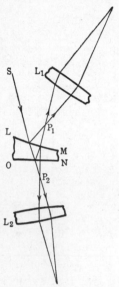

Fig. 93.—Interference at a thin film.

At perpendicular incidence the actual geometrical difference in path will be $d = 2a = y^2/R$, and when this is an odd multiple of a half wave, darkness would be expected if there were no other consideration. In fact this *is* the condition for darkness in the transmitted ring-system, but *not* for the reflected ring-system, for here the reverse intensity conditions are found. This is one evidence of a reversal in phase when light is reflected from the surface of a denser medium into a rarer. Because of this reversal in phase, there is brightness in the reflected system at points which are dark in the transmitted system and *vice versa*. Hence at places where

$$\frac{y^2}{R} = m\lambda \ (m = 0, 1, 2, 3, \text{etc.}),$$

there is darkness in the reflected system and brightness in the transmitted and wherever:

$$\frac{y^2}{R} = (m + \tfrac{1}{2})\lambda$$

the opposite conditions prevail. Values of y are the radii of the interference rings.

If white light is used the interference rings are colored. This is because white light consists of many wave lengths and at any given point a distance y from the center of contact, some wave lengths will have maximum and some will have minimum intensities. These wave lengths may be found by solving the formulae given above. In the reflected light, for example, the wave lengths given by

$$\lambda = \frac{y^2}{mR} = \frac{2a}{m}$$

will have a small intensity, while the wave lengths given by

$$\lambda' = \frac{2a}{m + \tfrac{1}{2}}$$

will have a maximum intensity. Intermediate wave lengths will have intensities ranging uniformly from maximum to minimum. This causes colors to appear. When $2a$ is small there are only a few visible wave length bands in the range from 0.000076 to 0.000038 centimeter which are reenforced or suppressed and the colors will be very brilliant. When $2a$ becomes large, however, there will be so many wave lengths reenforced and suppressed in the visible region that the balance between the primary color sensations will remain unchanged and the mixture will appear white. For this reason the colors are seen with their greatest brilliancy when the thickness of the film is only 0.0002 to 0.0008 millimeter. When the film is thinner than 0.0002 millimeter the colors disappear, because there is not enough variation in the intensity of the primary colors.

In the case of the transmitted rings, the wave lengths which were suppressed in the reflected light are now reenforced, while the wave lengths before reenforced are now suppressed. Hence the colors transmitted and reflected are exactly complementary at any point.

101. Thick Parallel Plates.—If the film is thick, or the light incident at too oblique an angle, the interference bands will be indistinct even in monochromatic light. The reason for this is that the two coherent rays of each pair are too far apart or of too great a divergence to be focused on the retina. To observe interference with a large difference in path, as in a thick plate, the incident rays must be parallel. Figure 94 shows one experimental arrangement. A transparent plate of glass AB reflects part of the light from the source S into the plate $LMNO$ which reflects some of it back from each surface. The reflected pairs of rays are then focused by the lens L to some point, as P, according to their inclination. These pairs of rays will form two sets of coher-

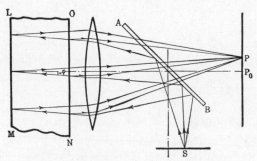

Fig. 94.—Fringes of constant inclination.

ent rays of which one is reflected from LM and the other from ON, the rays having the same inclination with the normal. The path difference between the rays of each of these pairs will be the same and there will be brightness or darkness at P, according to the value of the path difference. Other coherent pairs of rays having other inclinations with the normal will be focused at other points. Since the phase difference depends on the angle the rays make with the normal, the interference fringes will be circles about P_0 which is the focus of rays which are reflected normally. These are called Haidinger's fringes or "fringes of constant inclination." Fringes such as Newton's are called "fringes of constant thickness of film." The thinner the plate, the larger and farther apart Haidinger's fringes will be. If the plate is wedge shaped, they may have various shapes depending on the angle of incidence and the angle of the wedge, sometimes being practically straight.

102. Interferometers.—Interference fringes are used very frequently for the purpose of studying small motions and for spectroscopic analysis of radiation. Thus, for example, Fizeau invented a dilatometer for measuring coefficients of expansion of small pieces of material, especially of crystals. As shown in Fig. 95, a plane surface is supported by a tripod resting on the crystal, while another surface is held close over it by a tripod of long screws reaching through the base. The screws are adjusted so as to get a set of interference fringes between the surfaces. As the apparatus is heated, the fringes move gradually as the thickness of the air space changes. A motion of one fringe space means an expansion equal to half a wave length of the light used, since darkness reappears at a point whenever the distance $a = m\lambda/2$. By measuring small displacements of the fringes by means of a micrometer microscope, very high accuracy may be reached by this method. The expansion measured in this way is, of course, the relative expansion of the crystal and supports, and to get that due to the crystal alone, one must determine the part of the expansion due to the various supports. This is done by using some material whose coefficient is known accurately.

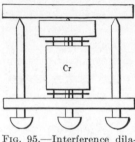

FIG. 95.—Interference dilatometer.

Of the large number of other instruments employing interference perhaps the most important is the Michelson interferometer. Referring to Fig. 96, a half-silvered mirror M_1 separates the light falling on it into two beams traveling at right angles to each other. These are reflected back along their original paths by the mirrors M_2 and M_3 so that the light which enters the eye at E is focused together and interferes according to the phase conditions. A plane parallel plate P is placed between M_1 and M_2 to make the optical paths in the two arms of the instrument equal when the actual geometrical distances are equal. With this plate in the proper place there are three passages through glass by each of the interfering beams. The mirror M_3 is mounted on a screw so that it may be moved forward or backward. The interference may be considered virtually to take place in the space between M_3 and the image M_2' of M_2 in the mirror M_1. Hence all that was said about interference in a thick parallel plate applies to this case as well. Usually it is most convenient to adjust M_2 and M_3 at very small angles to each other so that the fringes appear as vertical lines. As M_3 moves, these fringes move across the field. For a motion of half a wave by M_3, the fringes move a distance equal to the space between them.

With such an interferometer, Michelson measured the length of the standard meter at the International Bureau of Weights and Measures, in terms of the wave lengths of certain radiations

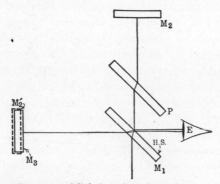

Fig. 96.—Michelson interferometer.

from luminous cadmium vapor. Prismatic analysis of this light reveals three strong wave lengths, respectively, in the red, green, and blue parts of the spectrum. These wave lengths depend solely on the atomic structure of cadmium and are probably as unchangeable quantities as can be found. Using these waves, Michelson found that there were 1,553,163.5 of the waves of the red radiation, 1,966,249.7 of the green, and 2,083,372.1 of the blue in 1 meter. The results are reduced to 15°C. and are in air at normal atmospheric pressure. The details of the method used in making these measurements are given in Michelson's book entitled "Light Waves and Their Uses."

The interferometer can also be used to measure the thickness of thin transparent films placed in one of the interfering paths. The fringes are displaced by an amount corresponding to the increase in optical path caused by introducing the film. This amounts to $2(n - 1)d$, where n is the index of refraction of the film, 1 is the index of the air which it replaces, and d is the thickness. This motion of the fringes may be compensated by moving the mirror M_3 through the linear distance $(n - 1)d$ or by rotating a compensating plate. When white light is used, one obtains a single colorless band when the paths of the two arms are exactly equal. This fact is used in determining when the change in optical path produced by the insertion of the film has been entirely compensated. As one interesting application of the method, may be cited the measurement of the thickness of soap films just before breaking. Using 50 such films in line, Michelson found that the thinnest soap film obtainable was about six-millionths of a millimeter in thickness. Since the film must have been at least two molecules thick, it is certain that the soap molecules are smaller than three-millionths of a millimeter. The diameter of the hydrogen atom is about 2×10^{-8} centimeter.

If the radiation from the source used with the interferometer is not all exactly of one wave length, the intensity of the interference fringes will vary as M_3 is moved slowly by rotating the screw. Michelson has developed the theory of this variation, and used it to analyze a number of composite spectrum lines which could not be easily separated into their components. A very simple example is that of sodium light. Any good spectroscope shows that there are two spectrum lines very close together in the orange. If sodium light is used to illuminate the interferometer, these two wave lengths give two sets of bands of slightly different spacing. These bands will fall on top of each other for some positions of M_3, where the effect is to strengthen their visibility, and will fall side by side for other positions so that the fringes nearly vanish. The differences between the two wave lengths may be found by observing the displacements of M_3 associated with the periodic changes in visibility.

The maximum difference in path for which interference can be obtained is about 1,200,000 waves. The emitting mechanism of the atom evidently sends out, on the average, only that many waves at a time. It probably stops emitting due to diminishing energy or due to a collision. This number of waves is emitted in a time of less than one-hundred-millionth of a second and explains why light must come from coherent sources before visible interference is possible.

A large Michelson interferometer has also been used in experiments designed to measure the motion of the earth through space. Einstein's theory of relativity is based on the result obtained. This will be taken up in Chap. XIV.

103. Industrial Interferometer.—A portable interferometer which can be used for the analysis of gases or liquids has been placed on the market. The instrument has a different form from that of the Michelson interferometer but in principle it is the same. Two tubes closed by plane glass ends are placed in the respective "arms" of the interferometer. One tube contains the substance to be tested, while the other contains some convenient reference standard—whose chemical composition differs in a simple manner from that of the unknown. The white-light interference fringes are used and the turns and fractions on the compensator screw which are needed to bring the central achromatic fringe on the cross-hairs are determined. The reading depends on the difference in optical path in the two tubes and this depends on their length and the difference in the indices of the two substances being compared. This difference in the indices depends on the concentration of the unknown component in the solution or mixture. The compensator screw can be calibrated in terms of percentages of the unknown. Such interferometers are used in some industrial laboratories to check the purity or strength of a product. They are also used in some hospitals and medical laboratories to measure such things as CO_2 concentrations in exhaled air, which depend on metabolism, and also for measuring percentages of other substances such as albumin. In short, this type of interferometer is merely a very delicate refractometer and can be used on similar problems. However, changes in index of refraction of one-thousandth part of the smallest detectable by total reflection methods can be measured by the interferometer.

104. Stationary Light Waves.—When homogeneous light is reflected normally by a polished surface, standing waves are produced by the combination of the incident and the reflected light. This phenomenon is similar to the production of standing waves in the case of sound and the formation of nodes and loops on a vibrating string. Since the wave length of light is very short, the nodes and loops are very close together in this case.

Hence it is hard to observe them.　Wiener, however, succeeded in obtaining a photographic record of stationary light waves by means of a very thin collodion film AB (Fig. 97), inclined to the surface of a mirror AM.　When the film was developed, dark and light lines were found running parallel to the line of intersection of the film and mirror.　These are evidently at the loops of the standing waves as shown in the figure.　The finding of a dark band at a distance of $\lambda/4$ from the surface of the glass plate showed that the first node was at the glass surface.　There must have been, therefore, a reversal in phase at the reflection

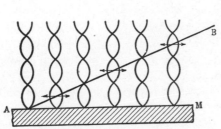

Fig. 97.—Stationary waves.

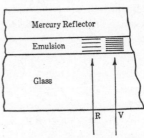

Fig. 98.—Lippman process of color photography.

thus confirming the conclusion based on the appearance of Newton's rings in reflected light as described in a preceding paragraph.

Standing light waves are the basis of a method of color photography invented by Lippman.　A very fine-grained photographic film, about five or ten waves thick, is placed against a mercury surface which acts as a mirror (Fig. 98).　The film is then exposed in a camera, the mercury being held in a reservoir behind the film.　On the other side, the film is, of course, supported by a plate of glass.　When the exposed film is developed, there will be layers of silver deposited at regularly spaced intervals in the film, the spacing being equal to half the wave length of the light falling on that particular portion of the film.　When white light falls on the finished plate, the colors not in harmony with the spacing will not be reflected very well because of interference, and only the original light will be seen.　The method is too difficult to be commercially practicable, but, nevertheless, it is possible to obtain beautiful results by this means.

Problems

1. Light from a single slit passes through a double slit with openings 0.45 mm. apart and interference fringes are formed on a screen 40 cm. away. If the fringes have a spacing of 0.386 mm., what is the wave length of the light? *Ans.* 0.0000431 cm.

2. If the single slit in the above problem is 40 cm. behind the double slit, how wide is it when the interference fringes vanish? (See page 121.) *Ans.* 0.386 mm.

3. Two plane surfaces of glass in contact along one edge are supported at the other edge by a strip of tinfoil. Fifty dark interference fringes are observed in sodium light (reflected); what is the thickness of the foil? *Ans.* 0.0147 mm.

4. A convex lens pressed against a plane surface gives interference fringes in sodium light. If the radius of the fortieth dark ring is 2 cm., what is the radius of curvature of the lens? *Ans.* 1698 cm.

5. A thin glass plate of index 1.55 is inserted in one arm of a Michelson interferometer causing a displacement of 300 fringes of sodium light. What is the thickness of the plate? *Ans.* 0.161 mm.

6. Why are the colors of thin films brightest when the films are neither too thin nor too thick? About how thick should they be? *Ans.* Order of magnitude of best thickness is the wave length of light (explained on page 126).

7. Interference bands between two surfaces in sodium light are used to study plant growth. When 20 bands have moved over the cross-hairs of the observing telescope, how much has the plant grown? *Ans.* Twenty half wave lengths of sodium light, or 0.00589 mm.

8. White light passes through a film 0.00005 cm. thick. What is the approximate color of the transmitted light? *Ans.* Visible reinforced wave length = 0.00005 cm.—therefore green.

9. The index of refraction of air is 1.000292 and that of CO_2 is 1.000484. What will be the difference in optical path through 50 cm. of the respective gases? *Ans.* 0.0096 cm.

10. In a gas interferometer the light passes twice through a tube 25 cm. long. If one can measure changes in optical path to one-tenth of a wave length of sodium light, what is the smallest difference in index of refraction that can be detected? *Ans.* 0.0000001178.

CHAPTER XI

DIFFRACTION

105. Propagation of Light.—According to Huyghens' principle, a light wave is propagated as though each point on the wave serves as the center of a spherical wavelet, and the resultant wave at some later time is the envelope of the wavelets at that instant. In order to make his theory consistent with the rectilinear propagation of light, Huyghens supposed that the wavelets were effective only at the point where they touched the common tangent, or envelope, of the whole set. He could not say exactly why this should be, except that it gave the results he thought were right. In Fig. 20 is shown Huyghens' construction of the wave AB from a source at S traveling through a hole in an opaque screen. The secondary sources are all taken in the plane of the opening and the wavelets start from them at the respective times that the main disturbance reaches them. The envelope of all such wavelets is $A'B'$, which apparently extends only as far as common tangents can be drawn, and so, according to Huyghens, the shadow is perfectly sharp.

There are several objections to the theory outlined above. One of these is that since sound is a wave motion, it should also obey this principle and give sharp shadows analogous to those of light. It does not do this. The chief objection, however, is that sometimes we can see very clearly that light does not travel in perfectly straight lines. These objections are met in Fresnel's modification of Huyghens' principle in which he simply applies the principle of interference to the Huyghens' wavelets. This idea explains the approximately rectilinear propagation and also the actual bending of light, which is called *diffraction*.

Referring to Fig. 99, let S be the source of a wave which is at AB at some instant, and let P be a point in the path of the wave. Huyghens' wavelets come like ripples from all points of AB and arrive at P with various inclinations and phases. If the differences in their paths are odd multiples of a half a wave length, the wavelets will oppose each other, the interference being only partial, however, because the amplitudes are not equal. To analyze this interference, Fresnel regarded the wave AB as divided into half-wave zones according to the distances D from

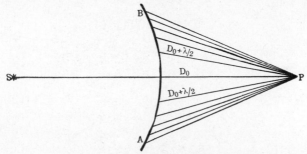

Fig. 99.—Fresnel zone theory.

the point P. Thus, if D_0 is the shortest distance from the wave to P_0,

the first zone lies between $\quad D = D_0 \text{ and } D = D_0 + \dfrac{\lambda}{2};$

the second zone lies between $D_0 + \dfrac{\lambda}{2} \text{ and } D_0 + 2\dfrac{\lambda}{2};$

the third zone lies between $\quad D_0 + 2\dfrac{\lambda}{2} \text{ and } D_0 + 3\dfrac{\lambda}{2};$

the mth zone lies between $\quad D_0 + (m - 1)\dfrac{\lambda}{2} \text{ and } D_0 + m\dfrac{\lambda}{2}.$

Thus, the average distances of the various zones from P increase progressively by half a wave length. Hence, all the even-numbered zones will send wavelets to P in the opposite phase to all those from the odd-numbered zones. If a_1 represents the amplitude of the effect from the first zone, and a_2 that from the second, and so on, then the amplitude at P will be

$$A = a_1 - a_2 + a_3 - a_4 + \cdots \pm a_n.$$

Because of increasing inclination and distance, the light effect reaching P from these zones will rapidly decrease so that only the first eight or ten are of any importance. The decrease in amplitude is regular, so that if we put A in the form

$$A = \tfrac{1}{2}a_1 + (\tfrac{1}{2}a_1 - a_2 + \tfrac{1}{2}a_3)$$
$$+ (\tfrac{1}{2}a_3 - a_4 + \tfrac{1}{2}a_5), \text{ etc.,}$$

all the terms except the first may be neglected. Therefore it is possible to write $A = \tfrac{1}{2}a_1$. This proof of Fresnel's is not free from objections mathematically, but it nevertheless leads to the right result. The rigorous deduction of this result is too difficult to give here. The amplitude at P is accordingly equal to half of what it would be if due to the first zone alone. Since the energy in any periodic motion varies as the square of the amplitude, this means that the intensity at P will be only one-quarter of what it would be if only the first zone were illuminating

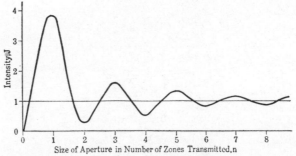

Fig. 100.—Intensity on a line through the center of a round hole.

the point. It must be understood that this result refers only to the single point P and in no way implies what conditions hold at points around P. If the first two zones alone are effective, the intensity at P will be nearly zero, because of interference. For the first three, it will be larger than the average but not so large as a_1, since the amplitudes from the outer zones decrease rapidly. As the number of zones is increased, the intensity at P gradually approaches that due to the entire wave. In Fig. 100 is given a graphical representation of the intensity at P plotted against the number of zones uncovered as abscissas. These effects are easily verified, at least qualitatively, by examining the beam of light from a small source S after passing through holes of various sizes. The effect is clearest in monochromatic light. If the source S is not small, the bands will also be indefinite because of blurring over due to light from the various parts of the source.

If white light is used, the variation of intensity at P will result in a change of color at P as the size of the hole is increased. This happens because for different wave lengths, the zone sizes are naturally different, and so the variation in intensity is different.

Because of the shortness of the wave of light, the radii of the zones will be very small unless P is very far away. For a distance D_0, the outer radius r_m of the first m zones is

$$r_m = \sqrt{\left(D_0 + m\frac{\lambda}{2}\right)^2 - D_0^2} = \sqrt{mD_0\lambda + m^2\frac{\lambda^2}{4}} = \sqrt{mD_0\lambda} \text{ (nearly)}.$$

For ordinary light ($\lambda = 0.000055$ centimeter) and a distance of 1 meter, this is equal to $r_m = 0.74\sqrt{m}$ millimeter. A set of diaphragms prepared according to this formula, so that they respectively admit 1, 2, 3, 4, etc., zones, will show that a point P on the axis 1 meter away is dark when m is even and bright if m is odd.

When this theory was first presented by Fresnel, another French scientist, Poisson, objected to it on the grounds that if a circular disc obstructed the first few zones, there would still be light from the outer zones at the center of its shadow cast by a small source S. He thought it absurd to suppose that the center of the shadow cast by a disc should be bright. Arago, however, tried the experiment. He found the bright spot and immeasurably strengthened Fresnel's theory.

These effects are not very hard to demonstrate if the source is a small hole in front of an arc or a small, highly polished ball in the light beam, and if the shadow is either cast on a screen or viewed directly by an eyepiece held in front of the eye. If it is not practicable to perform the experiment, a set of photographs made by students of Arkadiew[1] may be consulted.

106. Diffraction Bands.—When the experiments described above are repeated, or photographs of the effects examined, not only changes in illumination of the center P will be noticed, but also rings of alternate light and darkness around it. If, however, the hole is exceedingly tiny, there is simple spreading without maxima and minima. In the case of the disc experiment,

[1] *Phys. Zeit.*, Vol. XLV, p. 832.

FIG. 101.—The edge of the shadow of a straight edge using a narrow source of light (see Fig. 102).

bands will be seen outside of the shadow as well as fine narrow rings around the central spot. All of these bands are called *diffraction bands* and are caused by the interference of the wavelets from the various zones of a wave front. To determine whether any point is to be bright or dark, that point is taken as the center for the construction of zones and then it is determined whether these will add up to give a greater or a lesser intensity than normal. There are, naturally, precise mathematical methods for calculating the intensity but these are too difficult for an introductory course.

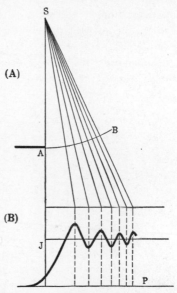

Fig. 102.—Diffraction of light from *S* at a straight edge *A*.

Now consider qualitatively the formation of diffraction bands by the straight edge of a large screen. A photograph of such bands is given in the frontispiece. Since only the first few zones are of importance, and since their outer radius is small, there will be the normal light and shadow conditions except at the very edge of the shadow where the edge of the screen partially cuts into the important central zones. Here there will be fluctuations in the amount of light, producing bands parallel to the shadow. Inside the geometrical shadow there will not be the perfectly abrupt decrease in intensity which strict rectilinear propagation would give, but rather a gradual decrease in intensity. Figure 102*A* shows the experimental arrangement, and 102*B* shows a graphical representation of the intensities at various points on the illuminated screen. The bands produced outside the shadow of any moderately large opaque screen are of this same general nature as long as the screen is large enough to cover up completely the eight or ten important zones. The bands take the shape of the shadow and are always parallel to it. In case of a small screen, however, the results are different because the entire boundary cuts into the important zones and not merely that part of the boundary whose shadow is being considered.

For an opening of several zones, the rings are in the bright region extending from the shadow boundary to the center P_0 where the intensity conditions vary in the manner described. For an opening of only one zone or less, the rings are all outside the central bright region, being in the region of the geometrical shadow, and the center P_0 is always bright. The size of the rings and central spot increases as the hole becomes smaller until finally they vanish entirely and there is only a diffusion of the light.

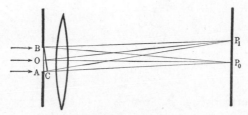

Fig. 103.—Diffraction by a slit.

107. A Narrow Slit in Parallel Light.—The diffraction pattern of a slit in parallel or nearly parallel rays is of interest because it applies to the theory of optical instruments. Suppose that the source is a filament parallel to the slit and is either far away, so that the incident wave is plane, or at the principal focus of a lens, which accomplishes the same effect. Suppose, too, that the screen is very far away compared with the width of the slit. This may also be done virtually by means of a lens on the other side of the slit (Fig. 103). Such diffraction effects in parallel light are called Fraunhofer's diffraction phenomena, while those considered before are called the Fresnel phenomena. In the case now under consideration, the zones in AB with reference to any point P will be strips parallel to the edges of the slit. At P_0 there will be brightness, because for plane waves the slit is all one zone with reference to this point. In fact, the center is always bright in Fraunhofer's diffraction phenomena for this reason. For some point P_1, however, the edge A will be just one wave farther from it than B, so that the slit will transmit two zones to this point.

These cancel each other completely because they have the same area, the same inclination, and travel nearly the same distance. At some point P_2, farther away, there will be brightness because the aperture will transmit three zones, of which two will cancel. This point will be bright, but evidently much fainter than P_0. (See Fig. 104A for a photograph of this effect.)

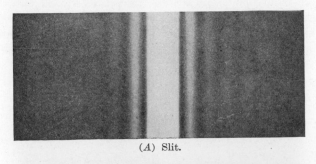

(*A*) Slit.

(*B*) Circular aperture.

FIG. 104.—Fraunhofer diffraction phenomena.

The above can be summed up by saying that if AC is an even multiple of a half wave, except zero, there will be darkness in the direction of AC, while if it is an odd number of half waves, there will be brightness. If θ is the angle of AC with the normal, then if a is the width of the slit

$$AC = a \sin \theta.$$

There is darkness when θ is such that

$$a \sin \theta = m\lambda \quad \text{where } m = 1, 2, 3, \text{ etc.,}$$

and brightness where

$$a \sin \theta = \frac{2m + 1}{2} \lambda \text{ or where } \theta = 0.$$

Because of brightness at $\theta = 0$, the central bright band is twice as wide as the rest. In this way the bands differ in appearance from interference bands. Because the wave length of light is so small, the distances $PP_0 = p$ will be small compared with the distance D from slit to screen. In this case $\sin \theta = p/D$, very nearly, and we have darkness at P when

$$p = m\frac{D\lambda}{a} \quad \text{except } p = 0,$$

and brightness when

$$p = \left(m + \frac{1}{2}\right)\frac{D\lambda}{a} \quad \text{and when } p = 0.$$

This means that, except for the center, a set of equidistant bands of spacing $D\lambda/a$ is observed. The central bright band has the width

$$2\frac{D\lambda}{a}.$$

In white light, in which λ varies from 0.00076 millimeter for the red to 0.00038 millimeter for the violet, the spacing of the fringes will vary proportionately. The fringes in white light will then be brightly colored except the central fringe.

108. Resolving Power.—The central band in the above may be regarded as the image of the source by the portion of the lens exposed by the slit. Similar considerations hold in the case of a round opening or even the entire lens for any sufficiently distant point source. In this case the bands take the shape of the opening; hence, there is formed a bright central spot with faint surrounding rings. This central spot is the image of the point source made by the lens whose diameter is a (see Fig. 104B). Figure 105 shows a graph of the intensity variation across the central disc and ring system. Even if the lens is absolutely perfect, this disc image has the diameter $2P_0P_1$ (Fig. 105), since it depends only on the wave length of the light, the aperture of the lens, and the distance to the image. The central spot is very small for a lens of any appreciable diameter but it exerts a very important effect on the fine structure of the lens image. This is especially noticed when the magnification is high. The diameter of the central spot is nearly the same as the width of the central band produced by a slit as derived above. This proved equal to

$$2\frac{D\lambda}{a}$$

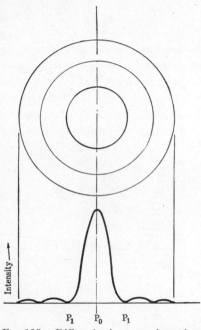

FIG. 105.—Diffraction by a round opening.

In fact, one might assume that *BOA* in Fig. 103 is a cross-section of a circular diaphragm and, using the same derivation, to come to the conclusion that the above expression gives the diameter of the central spot in the diffraction pattern. However, such a procedure would only give an approximate value because the zones are no longer parallel rectangular strips of equal area, being "mutilated" by the circular edge of the opening. For a round hole of diameter a, it can be shown that the exact expression is

$$2P_0P_1 = 2.44\frac{D\lambda}{a}.$$

When the rays come from two distinct object points, two such disc images are formed. If these images are so close together that the edge of one cuts through the center of the other, the two images can just be distinguished. If they overlap more, experience shows that the images unite to form one spot, and the points are said to be not resolved. The images will just be resolved if their centers subtend the angle $\alpha = P_0P_1/D$ at the lens. This angle is called the minimum angle of resolution and we see from the above that

$$\alpha = 1.22\frac{\lambda}{a}.$$

Since the stars are practically point sources, the equation above shows that close double stars will be better resolved by a large telescope than a small one. If the objective is not large enough to resolve the image, no amount of magnification will help, because this will only make the blurred, unresolved image larger. There must, however, be enough magnification to make any adjacent resolved points subtend an angle of at least 2 minutes of arc; otherwise the full resolving power is not utilized. Any magnification greater than this is an "empty magnification" yielding no new detail.

In the case of the microscope where the incident rays are not parallel, but highly divergent, the resolving power is most conveniently expressed by a different formula in terms of the so-called numerical aperture N of the objective, and the shortest linear distance d between points that are resolved. It is found that in this case

$$d = \frac{\lambda}{2N},$$

in which N, the numerical aperture, is equal to $n \sin A$, where n is the index of refraction of the medium between the lens and object, and A is the angle between a ray to the center and a ray to the edge of the lens. Now $n = 1$ for air, and $n = 1.6$ for oil-immersion microscopes, and since A must be smaller than 90 degrees, it follows that the numerical aperture cannot be larger than 1.6. Therefore, when the best possible resolving power is reached,

$$d_{min} = \frac{\lambda}{3} \text{ (approximately)}.$$

For visible light, $\lambda = 0.00055$ millimeter on the average, so that the smallest detail resolvable is 0.00016 millimeter. This assumes a perfect lens, for otherwise a resolving power as great as this cannot be obtained. This is a physical or objective resolving power and is entirely independent of the magnification. It merely gives the fineness of detail reproduced in the optical image. In order, however, to utilize the full resolving power visually, *i.e.*, subjectively, it is necessary that there be at least enough magnification to make the finest detail which exists in the image subtend about 2 minutes of arc at the eye. A magnification greater than this will be an "empty" one yielding no new detail. At 25 centimeters from the eye, an interval of 0.145 millimeter subtends an angle of 2 minutes. The greatest profitable magnification will be one that magnifies the smallest resolved interval up to 0.145 millimeter. If d_{min} is 0.00016, the greatest profitable magnification is 905. Higher magnifications are often used, but they are empty ones in so far as they exceed 905, even if the greatest possible resolving power has been reached.

The resolving power of an "ultramicroscope" is no greater than that of an ordinary one. An ultramicroscope is one in which the direct beam from the condenser does not enter the microscope. Particles are seen by the light that they scatter, appearing as bright points against a dark background. In this way much smaller particles can be seen than with the ordinary microscope just as the dust particles in a room can be seen better if the light which illuminates them does not directly enter the eyes. Resolving power, however, refers to the separation of *two* particles close to each other, and in this regard nothing is gained by dark ground illumination.

The only feasible way in which a greater resolving power can be obtained is by using shorter wave lengths of light. Such wave lengths will not pass through ordinary glass and cannot be seen directly by the eye. Lenses have been constructed of fluorite and quartz and a photographic plate has been used to replace the eye. In this way the minimum interval resolvable has been halved and the greatest profitable magnification has been doubled.

109. Diffraction Grating.—By the use of a set of equidistant parallel openings, one may obtain bright and sharp diffraction effects which furnish the most accurate means for the measurement of wave lengths of light. Consider a plate containing such openings, as shown in Fig. 106, placed in parallel light, and suppose that a lens is used to focus the light on a screen. All the rays diffracted through an angle θ because of the spreading of the wavelets through the apertures, will be focused to the same point, where they will combine according to their phases. The relative retardation between adjacent rays having the same inclination will be the same over the whole plate and will equal $a \sin \theta$, where a is the distance between adjacent openings and θ is the angle of diffraction. Now if this retardation is any integral number of

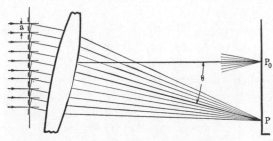

Fig. 106.—Diffraction grating.

waves there will be brightness at the point P where the rays come together. Hence there is brightness when

$$a \sin \theta = m\lambda.$$

In monochromatic light there will, accordingly, be a set of diffraction maxima for which $a \sin \theta = 1, 2, 3$, etc., wave lengths.

For only two openings separated by an interval a, the same results apply as far as the positions of maxima are concerned. There is, however, a very important difference in the appearance of the bands when the number of openings is large. In the latter case, the maxima are, naturally, very much brighter, but, what is more important, they are very much narrower. The width of the maxima varies inversely as the number of lines on the grating. With gratings of 20,000 or more lines, such as are used in optical work, the maxima are very bright and narrow, and since their position varies with the wave length, a spectrum of great purity is produced. The narrower the maxima, the greater is the resolving power for two nearly equal wave lengths, since their maxima are less likely to overlap. Hence, it is desirable to have as large a number of openings as possible.

A number of separate spectra will be formed for which $m =$ 1, 2, 3, etc., respectively. These are called the spectra of the first, second, third, etc., *order*. The lengths of the spectra increase with the order. This causes a higher resolving power in the higher orders. There is, however, considerable overlapping of the higher orders with each other since they soon become longer

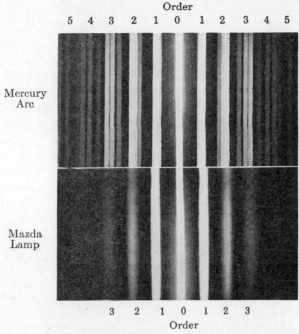

FIG. 107.—Diffraction grating spectra.

than their spacing. The spectra also become very weak in the high orders. The relative distribution of intensity in any small group of orders can, however, be adjusted by ruling grooves of the proper width and spacing.

Figure 107 is a photograph of such spectra taken with a rather coarse grating of 50 lines to the millimeter. The upper spectra show the sharp images of the slit by the several wave lengths from a mercury arc, showing increasing resolution in the higher orders. It is also seen that the mercury arc radiates shorter wave lengths than the Mazda lamp.

If θ is small, we can put $\sin \theta = p/D$, where D is the distance between the grating and the screen and $p = PP_0$. The maxima at P satisfy the condition

$$p = m \frac{D\lambda}{a}.$$

The displacement of the maxima is therefore proportional to the wave length for any given order. A spectrum in which such a simple proportionality holds is called a normal spectrum. A prism does not give a normal spectrum because of the greater dispersive power in the blue and the violet than in the red.

Diffraction gratings are generally used to measure wave lengths of light accurately. In order to increase dispersion, the lines should be close together. To get a large resolving power, there should be many of them. Gratings are often ruled with 14,000 to 25,000 lines to the inch, the grating sometimes being several inches wide. The type of grating whose action has been described above is known as a *transmission grating*. It is usually made by ruling lines on a plane parallel plate of glass with a fine diamond point. A very accurate screw automatically carries the plate along by a small fraction of a turn between scratches. The smooth spaces between the rulings are the openings considered above. The rest of the light is diffusely scattered.

Gratings are often ruled on mirrors of speculum metal to produce spectra by reflection. These are called *reflection gratings*. The greatest development of gratings for optical purposes has been made by Henry Rowland. He constructed the first accurate ruling engine, and his gratings are famous throughout the scientific world. His tables of measurements of wave lengths were acknowledged standards in the field of spectroscopy until replaced by Michelson's more accurate values. His greatest contribution to this subject is probably the invention of the concave grating, which has made a number of advances possible. This is a grating ruled on a concave mirror of speculum metal, often mounted in the manner shown in Fig. 108. The spectrum

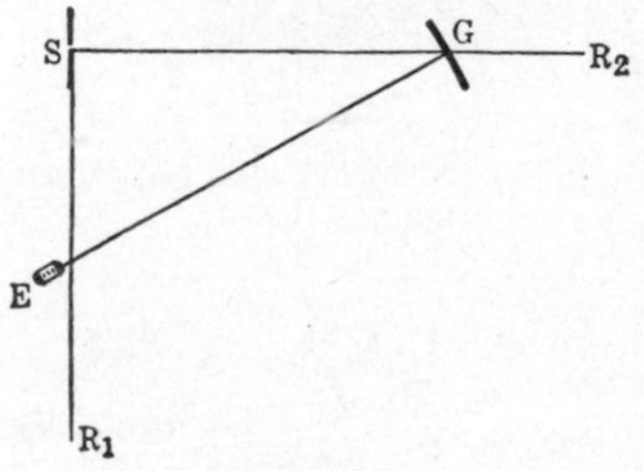

FIG. 108.—Rowland's mounting of concave grating.

lines are seen in the eyepiece as it is moved along the rail R_1. The grating G is continually kept at the right distance and at the proper angle to keep the lines in focus at the eyepiece E, both grating and eyepiece being attached at the ends of a rigid diagonal bar the ends of which are on wheels rolling along the two rails R_1 and R_2. The eyepiece may be dispensed with and the spectrum received on a photographic plate or film without the aid of any lenses. The plate or film must be bent in the arc of a circle having a diameter equal to the radius of curvature of the grating, which is the same as the length of the diagonal bar. Concave gratings are sometimes made with a radius of curvature of 20 feet. Among the advances made possible by this type of grating are ultra-violet spectroscopy in the region of extremely short waves, study of the fine structure of spectrum lines, and the influences of powerful magnetic and electric fields on atoms emitting light. All this information has an important bearing on atomic structure, one of the modern problems in physical optics.

Problems

1. What must be the size of a circular opening in a screen so that it will transmit two Fresnel zones to a point 2 m. away? What will be the approximate intensity of light at this point? (Assume wave length = 0.0000589 cm.) *Ans.* (a) dia. 0.308 cm.; (b) about zero.

2. Light from a distant point source passes through a circular opening whose radius is 1 mm. At what points will the opening exactly subtend, 1, 2, 3, 4, and m zones in sodium light? *Ans.* Distances, 169.8, 84.9, 56.6, 42.5, 169.8/m cm.

3. It is found that the distance between the first and eleventh dark diffraction band produced by a single slit 1 mm. wide on a screen 50 cm. distant is 2.75 mm. What is the wave length of the light? *Ans.* 0.000055 cm.

4. In the second order spectrum produced by a diffraction grating set normal to the incident light, a spectrum line at an angle of 30° with the normal is observed. If the grating has 4,000 lines to the centimeter, what is the wave length of the light? *Ans.* 0.0000625 cm.

5. What must be the diameter of a telescope objective in order that it will just resolve a double star subtending an angle of 1 sec. of arc? *Ans.* 13.8 cm.

6. What must be the numerical aperture of a microscope objective in order that it will just resolve two points which are one wave length (0.000055 cm.) apart? What magnification is needed to render the resolved detail perceptible to the eye? *Ans.* $N = 0.5$; $M = 264$.

7. It is desired to resolve structures involving separations of 0.00012 mm. Can this be done with visible light? Why? What wave length will be required? *Ans.* No. See page 144. 0.00036 mm.

CHAPTER XII

DOUBLE REFRACTION AND POLARIZATION

110. Double Refraction.—When a beam of ordinary light passes into some crystals, it separates, under certain conditions, into two beams which are refracted through different angles. This property of crystals is called *double refraction.*

This phenomenon is only one evidence of the difference between crystalline and ordinary matter. In general, it may be said that crystalline matter differs from ordinary in that at least one of its numerous physical properties is different in different directions. This variation in properties with direction manifests itself in the geometrical form in which the crystal grows. As the crystal forms by deposition from a solution or from the molten substance, it assumes a regular geometric form. If the growth is hampered so that it is not uniform in all directions, the faces may not be complete, but the portions present will make the same angles with each other. In the discussion of crystal form, a perfect crystal individual will be assumed.

Since 1912, it has been possible to measure the distances between atoms of crystals by the diffraction of X-rays as first demonstrated by Laue, Friedrich, and Knipping. In this way it is found that the external form is a direct consequence of the spatial distribution of atoms inside. Hence, crystals can be classified either according to their geometrical form (which was the only way before 1912), or according to the nature of the spatial arrangement of atoms. One can always select a unit of structure, which is the smallest group of atoms which contains all the kinds of atoms and all the kinds of bonds in the crystal. This unit is such that the entire crystal can be regarded as built up of a large number of such units placed side by side. In Fig. 109 is shown the unit of structure of zinc blend (ZnS).

The form of the unit of structure determines to which of the seven crystallographic systems the crystal belongs. Six of the seven standard forms are parallelopipeds having various angles between edges and various relative lengths of edges. Let us designate the lengths of the three edges which meet at any corner by *a*, *b*, and *c*. When the edges are at right angles, the crystal belongs to one of three crystallographic systems: the cubic, if $a = b = c$; the tetragonal, if $a = b \neq c$; and the ortho-rhombic, if $a \neq b \neq c$. When only two

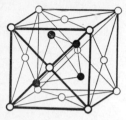

edges are at right angles, the crystal belongs to the monoclinic system regardless of the values of *a*, *b*, and *c*, while if none of the edges are at right angles, the crystal is said to be *triclinic*, unless $a = b = c$ and the angles between edges at two opposite corners are equal to each other. In this case the crystal is said to be *rhombic*.

ZnO   S●

The seventh system is one in which the unit of structure has a hexagonal cross-

Fig. 109.—Unit of structure of zincblend.

section and is called the *hexagonal system*. The rhombic system is sometimes regarded as a special class in the hexagonal system.

Crystals belonging to the cubic system are not doubly refracting, while all others are. When light is passed through a doubly refracting crystal in various directions, it is found that there is sometimes one direction and sometimes two, in which the light may travel without separating into two rays. Any such direction is called an *optic axis*. Crystals belonging to the rhombic, tetragonal, and hexagonal systems have one optic axis. In the latter two it is normal, respectively, to the square and the hexagonal cross-section. These crystals are said to be *uniaxial*. Crystals belonging to the orthorhombic, monoclinic, and triclinic systems have two optic axes and are, therefore, said to be *biaxial*.

Crystals of calcite ($CaCO_3$) show a bigger double refraction than any other common crystal. Hence, they are often used in optical apparatus which makes use of this effect. Calcite is classified as belonging to the rhombic system. The external form of the crystal is a rhomboid with, occasionally, beveled edges and truncated corners. An axis of symmetry *A* of period three passes through the most obtuse of its corners, as shown in Fig. 110.

This line and any one parallel to it is an optic axis, *i.e.*, a direction of no double refraction. A ray in any other direction will divide into two rays.

There is, quite obviously, a difference in the laws of refraction for the two rays. In a uniaxial crystal, like calcite, one of the rays obeys the ordinary laws of refraction. It always stays in the plane of incidence and has a constant ratio for the sines of the angles of incidence and refraction for all angles of incidence. The other ray does not always remain in the plane of incidence

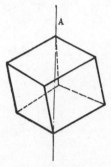

Fig. 110.— Rhomb of Iceland spar.

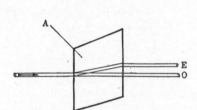

Fig. 111.—Double refraction.

and does not always have the same value for the sine ratio. Even if the light falls perpendicularly to the surface of a plane parallel plate of calcite, one of these rays will be refracted to the side, as shown in Fig. 111, unless the surface is parallel to the optic axis. Of the two rays produced at the refraction, the one that obeys the regular laws is called the *ordinary ray*, while the other is called the *extraordinary ray*. Experiment shows that the plane of the two rays is always parallel to the optic axis. Such a plane is said to be a *principal plane* of the crystal. If the crystal is rotated around the ordinary ray, the extraordinary ray will rotate around it, as Fig. 111 would suggest.

In a biaxial crystal, both of the rays are extraordinary, since neither of them obeys the ordinary laws of refraction for all angles.

111. Ray-velocity Surfaces.—A prism of doubly refracting material will give a double spectrum. By measuring the angle of the prism and the angle of minimum deviation, the index of refraction may be found for either of the two waves and for any color. Using many prisms having different orientations with respect to the crystallographic axes, one may find how the indices of refraction for the two rays vary with the direction of the rays. One finds that the velocity of the ordinary ray is the same in all directions, while that of the extraordinary ray is not. In the case of biaxial crystals, it is found that both of the rays travel with different velocities in different directions. The variations in velocity, however, follow perfectly definite laws which one can determine experimentally in this way.

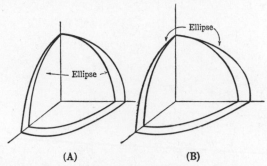

(A)   (B)

Fɪɢ. 112.—Uniaxial ray velocity surfaces.

Whenever a quantity depends on direction like the velocity of light in a crystal, it is customary to represent it by a plot in polar coordinates. This gives a surface, any radius vector of which represents the velocity in magnitude and direction. In the case of a uniaxial crystal there is obtained in this way, a spherical ray velocity surface for the ordinary ray and an ellipsoidal surface for the extraordinary ray. These two surfaces are tangent to each other at two diametrically opposite points. The line joining these points is a direction in which the two rays have the same velocity and is, therefore, the optic axis.

Two types of uniaxial ray surfaces are observed. In one of them the ellipsoid of the extraordinary ray velocity lies inside the sphere of the ordinary ray velocity, as in Fig. 112*A*, while in the other case the conditions are the reverse, as in Fig. 112*B*. The figures show only octants of the surfaces, since the other parts are the same. Crystals having the first type of refraction are said to be positively uniaxial; those of the second, negatively uniaxial.   Examples of these two types are, respectively, quartz and calcite.

In the case of a biaxial crystal, the ray surface is of a more complicated form.   Figure 113 shows one octant.   The sections

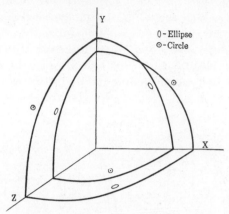

0 - Ellipse
⊙ - Circle

FIG. 113.—Biaxial ray velocity surface.

with the three planes of symmetry, namely, the XY, YZ, and XZ planes, are shown complete in Fig. 114.   One of the sections by each of these planes is in each case a circle, while the other is

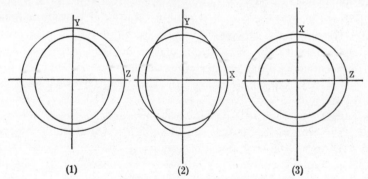

(1)   (2)   (3)

FIG. 114.—Sections of biaxial ray velocity surface.

an ellipse.   The discovery of the form of the ray surface is due to Fresnel, who also derived the mathematical expression for it.   The three radii of the circular sections are by pairs the axes of the three elliptical sections.   In fact, these are the three principal axes of the complete ray surface, and really determine the form of the surface, since the nature of its curvature is known from experiment and Fresnel's theoretical equation. It is seen that there are two directions of single ray velocity in a biaxial crystal, these being the two optic axes. The velocity in this direction is that given by the radius vector of the middle circle. The radii of the three circles give the three principal velocities. From them, the three principal indices are easily found by dividing them into the velocity of light in free space. The values of these main indices for a few of the more common biaxial crystals for sodium light are given in Table VI.

TABLE VI

Crystal	n_a	n_b	n_c
Mica (muscovite)....................	1.5601	1.5936	1.5977
Potassium nitrate..................	1.3346	1.5056	1.5064
Sugar (cane).......................	1.5397	1.5667	1.5716
Tartaric acid......................	1.4953	1.5353	1.6046

In the case of uniaxial crystals, only two velocities and, therefore, indices are needed to describe the optical behavior, since the ellipsoid is one of revolution and one of its two axes is equal to the radius of the sphere. The two main indices for a few uniaxial crystals for sodium light are given in Table VII.

TABLE VII

	Ordinary	Extra-ordinary
Positive uniaxial:		
Quartz...................	1.5442	1.5533
Ice.....................	1.309	1.313
Negative uniaxial:		
Calcite (Iceland spar)......	1.6584	1.4864
Sodium nitrate...........	1.5874	1.5361

112. Laws of Refraction.—It has been seen that the laws of refraction by crystals deviate from the ordinary laws of refraction except in the case of the ordinary ray. The laws of refraction for the extraordinary rays are not easy to express in algebraic form, but are, nevertheless, perfectly definite, and can be derived by an application of Huyghens' principle to the problem. It has been shown that if the Huyghens wavelets are spherical, the ordinary laws of refraction follow as a necessary consequence (see chapter on Refraction). On the other hand, if the wavelets are not spherical, other laws will be found to hold. They will depend on the exact shape of the wavelet and on how it is oriented with respect to the surface. Knowing the shapes of the wavelets, all the results of crystal refraction can be explained, at least graphically, by the use of Huyghens' principle.

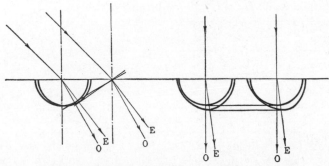

Fig. 115.—Huyghens' principle and double refraction.

Since the ray surfaces give the velocity of light in each direction, they have the form of a wave traveling out for a unit time from a point source at the origin. Thus, the form of a Huyghens wavelet in a crystal is the form of the ray velocity surface. It really consists of two wavelets having different forms and traveling with different velocities. Using this type of wavelet, Huyghens' principle can be applied to find the refracted waves in a crystal, as shown for a few cases in Fig. 115. The directions of the points of tangency from the centers of the wavelets are the directions of the rays. It can thus be seen that the ray is often not perpendicular to the wave, and that sometimes the refracted ray is not in the plane of incidence.

113. Polarized Light.—The different optical behavior of the two rays produced by double refraction suggests that they are physically different kinds of light waves. Further information in regard to their nature is obtained by passing them through a second crystal. When this is done, it is found that each of them separates into two rays, one of them an ordinary ray and the other an extraordinary ray, in case a uniaxial crystal is used. The rays produced by the separation of the ordinary ray will be designated as the *oe'* and the *oo'* rays, while those originating in the extraordinary ray will be called the *ee'* and the *eo'* rays. When the second crystal is rotated, there is not only a rotation of the *oe'* and *ee'* rays about the *oo'* and the *eo'* rays, respectively, but also a change in intensity of all four rays. In four positions of the second crystal, which are 90 degrees apart, it is found that one ray in each pair has a zero intensity while the other is at its maximum. This is illustrated by the following table of intensities:

	oe'	*oo'*	*ee'*	*eo'*
0°.............	zero	maximum	maximum	zero
90°.............	maximum	zero	zero	maximum
180°.............	zero	maximum	maximum	zero
270°.............	maximum	zero	zero	maximum
360°.............	zero	maximum	maximum	zero

Ordinary light coming directly from any source will not show any intensity variations when analyzed by a single crystal. There is consequently a difference between ordinary light and either of the two rays produced by double refraction. The intensity variation with angle of rotation shows that the latter have a polarity which ordinary light does not possess. Such rays are said to be *polarized*. It is to be noticed also that the same kinds of intensity variations occur when an analysis is made of either the ordinary ray or the extraordinary ray by the second crystal. The only difference is that, to duplicate in one beam the effects occurring in the other, the second crystal is rotated through 90 degrees. The ordinary and extraordinary rays are, therefore, said to be polarized at right angles to each other.

The physical nature of polarized light is easily understood when light waves are regarded as transverse. For, when the waves vibrate in a definite plane, the light wave evidently has a polarity. When the wave is composed of a mixture of vibrations in all conceivable planes, there is no preferred direction, and hence no polarity. Any ordinary source emits such a complex wave because there is a very large number of electrons vibrating in all directions with equal probability. When this mixture of waves passes into the orderly atomic arrangement in the crystal, the components of vibrations in some definite direction with respect to the crystal axes travel faster than the rest of the light. This part of the wave separates from the rest and travels along a different path, since direction of refraction also depends on velocity. The rest of the wave consists of the components at right angles to the first. These two parts of the original wave are the two doubly refracted waves, which are evidently polarized, and, moreover, are polarized at right angles to each other.

114. Polarization by Reflection.—Polarized light is obtained not solely by the use of crystals. When light is reflected from a polished surface of any electrical insulator, there is a preponderance of vibrations in a definite direction. In fact, a particular angle of incidence can always be found at which the polarization is practically complete. At other angles the polarization is said to be partial. The surface should be perfectly smooth and clean in order to be able to obtain complete polarization. The angle at which this occurs is called the *polarizing angle*. Brewster, who experimented with a large number of substances, found that the tangent of the polarizing angle p was always equal to the index of refraction n of the substance, so that

$$\tan p = n.$$

For crown glass of index $n = 1.6$, the polarizing angle is 57 degrees 20 minutes.

The polarization of reflected light can be demonstrated either by the use of a crystal or by a second reflecting surface inclined at the same angle with the incident beam, but capable of rotating around the beam, as shown in Fig. 116. If the reflection at the upper mirror takes place in the direction obtained when the planes of the mirrors are parallel as 116*A*, the light from the first is reflected twice as well as ordinary light would be. If, however, the two planes of incidence are at right angles as in 116*B*, none of the light is reflected by the second surface. This shows that the first reflection modifies the nature of the light beam in such a way that it is more easily reflected in a certain direction. In short, the light is polarized. This can also be demonstrated by means of the intensity variations observed when it is passed through a crystal which is rotated.

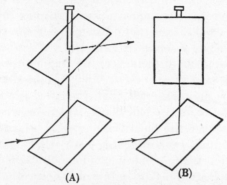

(A)   (B)

Fig. 116.—Polarization by reflection.

115. Planes of Vibration and Polarization.—By the theory of reflection of electromagnetic waves it can be proved that when light is polarized by reflection, the electric vibrations lie in a plane which contains the ray and is normal to the plane of incidence, while the mag-netic vibrations are in the plane of incidence. Thus, polarized light really has two vibration planes, but one of them is more important than the other. An experiment by Wiener on polarized stationary waves demonstrates this. Polarized light is reflected at an angle of 45 degrees by a metallic mirror covered by a photographic emulsion. The polarizing device can be rotated so that the vibrations have any angle with respect to the plane of incidence on the mirror. It is

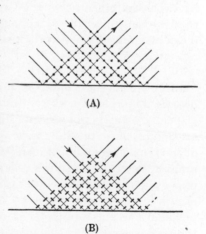

(A)

(B)

Fig. 117.—Interference of polarized light.

only for components of vibrations normal to the plane of incidence that there can be interference of the incident and reflected light

(Fig. 117*A*), for otherwise the reflected vibrations are perpendicular to the incident vibrations and cannot neutralize them, no matter what the phase may be (Fig. 117*B*).   In these figures the usual convention of representing vibrations normal to the plane of the paper by dots and in the plane of the paper by lines is used.   When the polarizer is so turned that the electric vibrations are in the plane of incidence, the magnetic will be at right angles to it, and *vice versa*.   Now, Wiener found that interference bands could be photographed only when the electric vibrations were normal to the plane of incidence, and not when the magnetic were.   Hence, only the electric vibrations can affect a photographic plate and very probably only they are effective in stimulating the retina.   The magnetic vibrations do not enter into such processes and it is only from theory that it is known that they must exist and always accompany the electric vibrations to which they are perpendicular.   In view of this, the term *plane of vibration* will be used with the understanding that the electric vibrations are the ones referred to.

To find the planes of vibration of the doubly refracted rays in crystals, reflect the light off a piece of glass at the polarizing angle. As explained above, this glass reflects only the vibration components which are normal to its plane of incidence, so that, if the incident vibrations are in the plane of incidence, no light will be reflected.   Conversely, if no light is reflected, the vibrations must be in the plane of incidence.   This is the standard method for finding vibration directions of polarized light.   It can be shown in this way that the extraordinary vibrations are always in a principal plane of the crystal while the ordinary vibrations are at right angles to that plane.   The principal plane may be defined as the plane of the two doubly refracted rays.   In uniaxial crystals it is always parallel to the optic axis.   In the case of biaxial crystals, the principal plane bisects the angle between the two optic axes.

Sometimes the term *plane of polarization* is used.   This plane is at right angles to the plane of vibration.   Thus the plane of polarization of light reflected at the polarizing angle coincides with the plane of incidence.   It was introduced in this sense before the vibration direction was known, and it is still used in many books.

116. Production of Polarized Light.—A beam of plane polarized light is often conveniently obtained by reflection of light at the polarizing angle by a plate of glass. The glass for this purpose is preferably black in order to avoid reflection from the inner surface which doubles the reflected images. This method is often used to obtain polarized beams of large cross-section.

The light transmitted through an inclined plate is found to be partly polarized at right angles to that reflected. To increase the percentage of polarization, a pile of thin transparent glass plates contained in a tube, as shown in Fig. 118, is used. Such an

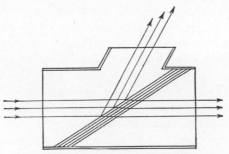

Fig. 118.—Polarization by pile of plates.

arrangement is sometimes convenient for projecting a direct beam of large cross-section on a screen. Each surface reflects about 7 per cent of the incident light, which is completely polarized, or nearly so. The transmitted remainder from each such reflection will, therefore, have an excess of the vibrations at right angles to those reflected, but the light will be far from completely polarized for a single plate. Each reflecting surface of each plate, however, tends to make the transmitted light more completely polarized.

To obtain plane polarized light by double refraction, one of the two beams must be removed. Crystals of tourmaline accomplish this by themselves, because they naturally absorb the ordinary ray. They are, however, strongly colored and, hence, not very efficient.

If the two beams in a calcite crystal are narrow enough, they will be entirely separated without overlapping, so that one of them can be blocked off by an opaque screen. This, too, is not a very efficient procedure, because a large beam cannot be obtained.

The usual method, and the best method, is to totally reflect one of the rays off a film of Canada balsam in the crystal. It has been shown (see Art. 53) that total reflection occurs only when light passes from a medium with higher index to one with a lower, and that even in this case the angle of incidence must be greater than some critical angle. Now the index of calcite is 1.6584 for the ordinary ray, and 1.4864 for the extraordinary. Canada balsam, a common optical cement, has an index of about 1.53 for both rays. It is therefore possible to totally reflect the ordinary ray in calcite off a balsam film in contact with the crystal, but not at all possible to do this with the extraordinary ray. In order to

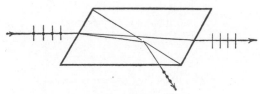

FIG. 119.—Nicol prism.

obtain the proper angle of incidence on the film, the ends of a calcite crystal are ground to certain angles and the crystal is cut in two diagonally. When cemented by Canada balsam along this cut, the ordinary ray will be totally reflected and absorbed in the black mounting of the finished crystal. A cross-section of such an arrangement is shown in Fig. 119. It was invented by Nicol, in 1828, and is commonly referred to as a nicol prism. It is the most efficient means for producing a strong beam of polarized light.

117. The Polariscope.—The polariscope is an apparatus for examining crystals, minerals, glass, and colloids in polarized light. It consists of a means for producing polarized light, which is passed through the substance, and is then analyzed by another polarizing plate or prism. The first plate or prism which produces the polarized light is called the *polarizer*, while that used for examining the final light is called the *analyzer*. Suitable lenses are often added to magnify the object or to project the light.

The action of the polariscope will first be considered with no substance between the polarizer and the analyzer.

These may consist of nicol prisms of which the second is capable of rotation, as indicated in Fig. 120. The amount of rotation cannot be shown easily in such a plane figure, since it is about an axis in the plane of the diagram; so it will be merely stated in words or shown in cross-section. The polarized beam produced by the first prism falls on the analyzer. If the principal planes of the two nicols are parallel, it will be transmitted, while, if they are perpendicular, none of it will pass through. Let α be the angle between the principal planes of the polarizer and analyzer. Measurements show that the intensity of the transmitted light varies as $\cos^2 \alpha$. Thus if I is the intensity of the

Fig. 120.—Polarizer and analyzer.

beam falling on the analyzer and I_e that of the transmitted beam, then, making allowance for the small absorption and reflection losses,

$$I_e = I \cos^2 \alpha.$$

If I_o is the intensity of the totally reflected beam as measured experimentally, then it is found that

$$I_o = I \sin^2 \alpha,$$

so that

$$I_o + I_e = I.$$

Now, the intensity of light is proportional to the square of the amplitude; hence it follows that

$$A_e = A \cos \alpha, \text{ and } A_o = A \sin \alpha,$$

showing that the analyzer, like any other crystal, performs a vector resolution of the incident vibrations into components respectively in and at right angles to its principal plane, as shown in Fig. 121A. There is only this difference in the two cases: a crystal transmits both of the rays, while a nicol prism transmits only the component A_e which vibrates in its principal plane. Moreover, A is always less than the incident amplitude because of absorption and reflection losses. This effect is the same as if a weaker source were used and the vibrations simply resolved without losses and therefore it will be overlooked.

The variation of intensity by the use of two nicol prisms is applied in the construction of some photometers. The illumination by a standard lamp can be conveniently reduced to any desired fraction by rotating one of the nicols instead of changing the distance of the lamp.

Suppose now that there is a crystal plate between the polarizer and the analyzer. Let ϕ represent the angle between the principal plane of the plate and the plane of vibration of the incident

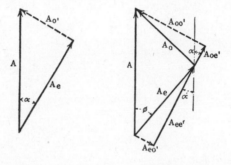

(A)   (B)

Fig. 121.—Amplitude components in polariscope.

light. If the crystal is doubly refracting, it will resolve the original amplitude into two parts, one vibrating parallel to its principal plane and the other at right angles to it as shown in Fig. 121B.
Then

$$A_o = A \sin \varphi, \text{ and } A_e = A \cos \varphi.$$

Now these two polarized beams pass into the analyzer. Let the angle between the principal planes of the analyzer and polarizer be α, as before. Both A_e and A_o will be resolved again but only A_{ee}' and A_{oe}' will be transmitted. These components, as shown in Fig. 121B, are the components of A_o and A_e in the principal plane of the analyzer. We have then

$$A_{ee}' = A_e \cos (\varphi - \alpha),$$

and

$$A_{oe}' = A_o \sin (\varphi - \alpha).$$

The angles are positive if clockwise as measured from the plane of the polarizer.

Now these finally transmitted rays are vibrating in the same direction and are, therefore, capable of interfering. The phase difference between these two rays will depend on the equivalent air paths in the crystal. Let n_o and n_e represent the indices of the crystal for the two rays, and let t be the thickness. The difference in equivalent air path will be

$$n_e t - n_o t = (n_e - n_o)t = d,$$

where d is the path difference. The fundamental formulae for interference (Chap. X) lead to the following equations: when there is no sudden phase reversal the intensity is a minimum whenever

$$(n_e - n_o)t = (m + \tfrac{1}{2})\lambda,$$

and a maximum when

$$(n_o - n_o)t = m\lambda.$$

On the other hand, if there *is* a phase reversal, the first equation gives the condition for a maximum intensity, while the second is for a minimum. To determine which way these equations should be used, a diagram such as Fig. 121B is drawn for the case under consideration. Starting with some definite direction for A as indicated by the arrow, one finds A_{ee}' and A_{oe}'. The directions of their arrows give the relative directions of vibration of the components. If the arrows on the transmitted components are in the same direction, as shown, there is no phase reversal and the equations are used in the first sense. Note, however, that for some directions of the principal plane of the analyzer, the arrows will be in opposite directions. This occurs, for example, if the analyzer is rotated by 90 degrees, so that the components totally reflected before will now be the ones transmitted. Hence it can be stated that for the totally reflected light, or the light transmitted when the nicol is rotated through 90 degrees, the equations cited for maximum and minimum intensity are to be exchanged.

If white light is used, one obtains interference colors for the reason explained before in the discussion of Newton's rings.

Briefly, this reason is that for any given path difference some wave lengths have a maximum and some a minimum intensity. Now, in the totally reflected light, there will be a minimum intensity for the same wave lengths which are at a maximum in the transmitted light. Hence the color of the totally reflected light will be complementary to that transmitted. Now the light totally reflected in any given case can be transmitted by rotating the analyzer through an angle of 90 degrees, so that the color complementary to that observed can always be obtained by rotating the analyzer through this angle.

The brilliancy of the colors observed varies when the angles φ and α are changed. Since the colors are due to the production, by interference, of minimum intensities for some wave lengths, they will be most brilliant if the minima are actual zeros, the maxima being as large as possible. These conditions occur only when the interfering amplitudes are equal and at the same time as large as possible. Hence, the brightest effects are observed when the principal planes of the polarizer and analyzer are parallel or perpendicular, with that of the crystal making an angle of 45 degrees with each of them.

It might seem that the interference colors could be produced even if the polarizer were removed. This is not the case. Unpolarized light consists of all kinds of transverse vibrations, so that one could obtain all kinds of vector resolutions in the crystal plate just as if the polarizer were used but continually revolved. If this is done slowly, it is found that the colors become complementary every 90 degrees of rotation. If the rotation is very rapid, the combination of the two colors is observed, and this is white. The same effect is observed without any polarizer. This was first pointed out by Fresnel and Arago after a thorough study of the conditions for interference of polarized light.

A piece of ordinary glass will not produce interference colors in a polariscope, because it is not doubly refracting. If, however, it is compressed, or if it has not been annealed to relieve the possible stresses produced by rapid cooling during its production, it will show double refraction. This effect is usually irregular, since it depends on the stress distribution in the substance. The polariscope gives a sensitive means for the detection of stresses in isotropic media, and is often used for this purpose.

118. Convergent Polarized Light.—Crystal plates in a polari-scope will produce different degrees of interference, either if they are cut from a crystal so as to have various orientations with respect to the optic axis or if the light is sent through them in different directions. When the light travels along an optic axis, the effect is the same as in the case of ordinary glass. If, however, the transmission is not in this direction, there will be double

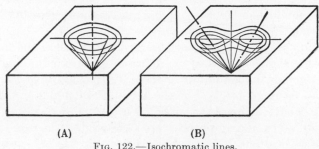

(A)   (B)

Fig. 122.—Isochromatic lines.

refraction with a path difference depending on the difference between the indices and the length of path through the crystal.

This variation in double refraction can be conveniently shown by the use of convergent or divergent light. In this way, rays pass through the crystal in various directions and these are focused at definite image points in the focal plane of a lens com-bination. Each point of the image shows the effect for some particular direction and distance of propagation in the crystal. The interference color produced will depend on the relative retardation, *i.e.*, on $(n_e - n_o)t$. If the crystal is uniaxial with the surfaces of the plate cut perpendicular to the optic axis both of the factors in this quantity increase with inclination. There will exist loci of constant path difference along which interference colors will be the same. These are called *isochromatic lines* or *isochromes*. In the case of uniaxial crystals cut perpendicular to the optic axis, the isochromatic lines are circles around the optic axis, as shown in Fig. 122*A*. In the case of biaxial crystals, the isochromes are more complicated, as shown in Fig. 122*B*. These two types of isochromes are seen in a polariscope when convergent or divergent light is passed through the crystal.

Dark brushes will also appear, cutting across the isochromes and obliterating them in places. These are due to the fact that the two beams produced in the crystal plate by double refraction are vector components of the original vibration; and one of these components vanishes for light going in certain directions. Examine a uniaxial plate, face on (Fig. 123). The circle represents the

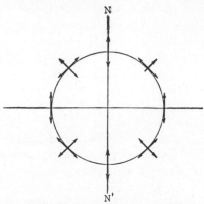

FIG. 123.—Isogyres of uniaxial crystals.

locus of emergence points of rays which make the same angle with the optic axis, but which differ in azimuth. The extraordinary rays will consist of the components which vibrate in a principal plane, *i.e.*, radially with respect to the optic axis in this case, while the ordinary vibrations will be in tangential directions. Let the incident light be vibrating in the direction of NN'. Its radial and tangential components are of various relative magnitudes and directions depending on the point of emergence. There will, however, be two lines in the figure, namely, NN' and a line at right angles to it, in which the original beam passes through unresolved. These two lines are loci of rays having a constant direction of vibration and are called *isogyres*. If the polarizer and analyzer are "crossed," *i.e.*, set for extinction, there will be a black cross in the directions of these isogyres. If the analyzer is rotated 90 degrees, the cross will be white, since now the nicols are parallel and transmit the vibrations of rays in the principal planes of the isogyres.

Similar considerations hold in the case of biaxial crystals, but the effect is not so simple. To find the direction of vibration of the components of the incident light, each axis may be treated as above, except that in resolving the incident vibration, the average is taken of the two radial and tangential directions by bisecting the angle between them. This construction gives isogyres crossing at right angles when the incident vibrations are perpendicular or parallel to the plane of the optic axes, but it gives hyperbolas if the incident vibrations are at 45 degrees.

119. The Polarizing Microscope.—The analysis of rocks, minerals, and crystals by the polarizing microscope has been so developed that the identity of the crystal constituents can be found by mere optical examination. For this purpose, a thin section about 0.01 millimeter thick is ground and polished. Practically all rocks are transparent when so thin. The tiny crystals are seen in the microscope in all kinds of orientations. Of these certain specimens showing maximum double refraction are selected for further observation. This method of rock analysis is called *petrography* or *optical mineralogy*.

The polarizing microscope has also been applied to the study of colloids and the structures of many constituents of plant and animal bodies. These are examples of non-crystalline materials which are, nevertheless, doubly refracting because of their peculiar structure. The use of polarized light sometimes gives information not obtainable by a microscope alone.

120. Circularly and Elliptically Polarized Light.—As has been shown, plane polarized light passing through a crystal plate separates into two components, respectively, in and at right angles to the principal plane, with the relative retardation $(n_e - n_o)t$. If the crystal plate is thin, these two rays do not emerge separately but combine into one ray having some definite resultant vibration. The resultant vibration of two simple harmonic motions at right angles is, in general, an elliptical vibration analogous to that of a pendulum vibrating in an elliptical orbit. The exact shape of the ellipse depends on the amplitudes of the component vibrations and on their phase difference. In certain special cases, the ellipse is so narrow that it may be considered to be a straight line, and sometimes the axes are so nearly equal that it becomes a circle. Figure 124 shows how two simple harmonic vibrations at right angles to each other may be combined graphically. It is based on the fact that the motion of the perpendicular projection on any line of a point moving uniformly in a circle is simple harmonic motion.   The two circular motions have the same velocity in order to give the same period (color of light) to the two vibrations.   The circles are uniformly divided into sixteen parts which represent sixteen successive positions of the point having circular motion.   These points are projected perpendicularly on the two lines AA' and BB' at right angles to each

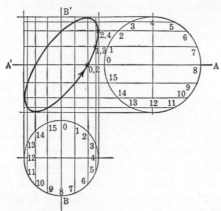

Fig. 124.—Composition of two vibrations at right angles.

other.   The resultant of the two vibrations is found by adding vectorially the two displacements of the projected point.   For example, let the relative retardation be $\frac{1}{8}\lambda$, i.e., one-eighth of a complete vibration.   When the A vibration is at 0, the other will be one-eighth of the way around from its corresponding point; in other words, at 2.   The two displacements are projected and added vectorially, giving the resultant at 0, 2.   One-sixteenth of a period later, the resultant will be 1, 3, and at an equal time later 2, 4, and so on.   The resultant vibration is given by the path through these points which is an ellipse, the shape of which depends on the two amplitudes and the phase difference.   If the two amplitudes are equal and the relative retardation is $\frac{1}{4}\lambda$, the vibration is circular.   The equal amplitudes necessary for this case are obtained experimentally by setting the crystal plate so that its principal plane makes an angle of 45 degrees with the incident vibration.   With a relative retardation of $\frac{3}{8}\lambda$ and the same amplitude relations, an ellipse sloping the other way is formed and this changes into a straight line as the retardation is increased to ½λ. Figure 125 shows the succession of types of vibration produced by a set of crystal plates at 45 degrees, having thicknesses which increase uniformly so that the phase differences are as given below each figure. The figure also shows how the state of vibration changes when light enters and travels in the crystal.

Plates of crystal which produce these effects under these conditions are called eighth-wave plates, quarter-wave plates, etc., respectively. They are usually made of mica and sometimes of selenite crystal.

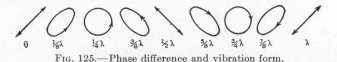

FIG. 125.—Phase difference and vibration form.

All of the effects shown in Fig. 125 can be produced by a single quarter-wave plate by turning it in the polarized beam. As the name implies, such a plate always gives a phase difference of ¼λ between the two rays; but their relative amplitudes can be varied by the position (rotation) of the plate in the beam.

A quarter-wave plate can also convert any elliptical vibration into plane polarized light when placed in the right position. This is an important property of the quarter-wave plate. Used in this way it is called an elliptic compensator and may be used to detect or to measure the vibration form of elliptically polarized light. The most important thing about the form of an ellipse is the ratio of the axes, and this may readily be found by means of a quarter-wave plate. The phase difference which produced it may also be determined if the principal plane of the unknown doubly refracting substance is known. Such measurements make polariscopic examination a quantitative method.

With respect to an ordinary nicol prism, elliptically polarized light behaves just like partially plane polarized light, so that the difference cannot be detected by means of a nicol alone. There is merely a fluctuation of intensity in both cases as the nicol is rotated. The distinguishing feature is the one just mentioned, namely, that an elliptic compensator will convert elliptically polarized light into plane polarized light which can be detected by a nicol. This is not possible with a partially plane polarized beam. In the same way, a circularly polarized beam appears to be an ordinary unpolarized beam when passed through a nicol prism, but here again a quarter-wave plate used in conjunction with a nicol enables one to detect the difference.

It is interesting to view a crystal in convergent circularly polarized light and with a circular analyzer. There are no isogyres in this light because there are no directions for which one component is missing. Hence, the black brushes are entirely absent, and the complete isochromatic lines can be seen.

121. Rotation of the Plane of Polarization.—If the two nicols of a polariscope are initially crossed so as to obtain extinction, it is found that some substances, when placed between them, simply rotate the position of the analyzer needed to produce extinction of the light. Thus the resulting light is still plane polarized, but the plane of vibration has been rotated through an angle equal to that through which the analyzer must be rotated to restore the original condition. Substances which produce this effect are said to be "optically active." Some of them rotate the plane of vibration in a clockwise direction as seen by an observer toward whom the light is traveling, while some rotate in the opposite direction. These are called, respectively, *dextro-* and *levo-rotatory* substances. Sometimes a single chemical substance appears in two forms with equal and opposite rotatory powers, as, for example, quartz.

The rotation of the plane of polarization by crystals is measured only in the direction of the optic axis so as not to be complicated by double refraction. A quartz plate cut perpendicular to the axis shows the rotation very well. In many crystals the rotation must be due solely to a peculiar crystal structure because the molten or dissolved structureless substance is inactive. The activity of quartz is of this type. In the case of quartz crystals, and many others, too, which crystallize in two forms which respectively rotate to the right and to the left, the two forms of crystal are exactly similar in appearance except that one is the mirror image of the other, like right and left gloves. In fact, any single crystal shows by its disposition of faces whether it is active or not, just as it shows by means of its crystal form whether it is uniaxial or biaxial. These principles concerning the relation of physical properties and crystal form were first recognized by Neumann and by Pasteur.

The angle of rotation by any active substance is proportional to the distance the light travels in the substance, and to its density, or concentration in case of solutions. The constant of proportionality is called the *specific rotatory power*. In the case of solids, the specific rotatory power is commonly expressed in units of degrees rotation per millimeter. The density specification is usually avoided by giving the temperature. Thus, for quartz at 20°C., the specific rotatory power for the orange sodium light is 21.70 degrees. It increases rapidly as the wave length becomes shorter. For the various Fraunhofer lines, quartz gives the following rotations per millimeter.

TABLE VIII

Fraunhofer line	A	C	D	E	F	G	K
Degrees per millimeter	12.67	17.32	21.70	27.54	32.77	42.60	52.15

The variation is nearly inversely as the square of wave length. This may be expressed by the following formula discovered experimentally by Biot:

$$[\alpha] = \frac{B}{\lambda^2},$$

where B is a constant for each substance. For quartz $B = 7.52$ when the wave length λ is expressed in microns (thousandths of a millimeter).

There are also many materials in which the rotation does not depend on crystal form since it is present even if the substance is molten or dissolved. In these cases the rotation is due to an unsymmetrical molecular structure. It is peculiar that such compounds nearly always contain carbon. The rotation is related to the unsymmetrical distribution of atoms or groups of atoms among the four valence "bonds" of carbon. The study of this phase of the subject has led to the development of the subject of stereochemistry, an important branch of organic chemistry.

122. Polarimetry.—The property of optical activity of substances in solution is often used in quantitative analysis. This especially applies to the sugars and tartrates. The instrument used for measuring the activity is the polarimeter, which is essentially a polariscope with a divided circle for measuring angles of rotation of the analyzer, and some kind of half-shadow device to increase the accuracy of the settings. Such a half shade is a crystal device which covers the halves of the field of view so that analyzer settings are made for equal intensity of both halves instead of for extinction.

To carry through the polarimetric analysis of sugar, for example, certain chemical operations must be carried out. These will be found described in most texts on organic or physical chemistry and also in a circular on Polarimetry issued by the Bureau of Standards. As already stated, the angle of rotation α is proportional to the length l of the tube holding the solution, and to the concentration p, so that

$$\alpha = [\alpha]lp,$$

where $[\alpha]$ is the constant of proportionality called the *specific rotatory power*. This is usually expressed in degrees per decimeter length of path for each gram of the active substance in a cubic centimeter of solution. It depends on wave length, temperature, impurities, and, slightly, on concentration. A few standard values for sodium light and a temperature of 20°C. are transcribed below from the Bureau of Standards circular.

TABLE IX

	Specific rotatory power
Sugars:	
Sucrose (cane).........	$+ 66.412 + 0.012673p$
Dextrose..............	$+ 52.50 + 0.0188p$
Fructose..............	$-113.96 + 0.258p$
Maltose..............	$+138.48 - 0.01837p$
Lactose..............	$+ 52.53$
Invert sugar..........	$- 19.447 - 0.06068p$

123. Rotation and Double Refraction.—When light passes through a quartz prism in the direction of the optic axis, there is a very slight double refraction which causes each spectrum line to be doubled. When the two spectra are tested by means of an elliptic analyzer, they are found to be circularly polarized in opposite directions. This experiment shows that the wave surfaces for the ordinary and extraordinary rays do not quite touch each other even on the optic axis so that a "circular" double refraction occurs. That is to say, the velocity of right-handed circularly polarized light is not the same as that for left-handed circularly polarized light along the optic axis of optically active crystals. This difference in velocity also occurs in all active solutions. Fresnel was the first to observe it in quartz and to point out that the rotation of the plane of polarization is,

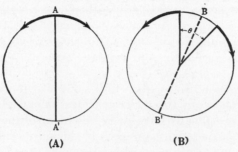

(A)   (B)

FIG. 126.—Fresnel's theory of rotation.

in fact, due to the difference in velocity of right-handed and left-handed circularly polarized rays. Thus, the incident linear vibration may always be resolved into two opposite circular vibrations having the same period. As shown in Fig. 126A, the sidewise motions in the two circular vibrations starting at A will neutralize each other and leave only the vertical motion AA'. If one of these vibrations travels faster than the other, it will get out of angular phase by, say, θ degrees with respect to the other by the time it emerges. As shown in Fig. 126B, the resultant will be another linear vibration but at an angle $\theta/2$ degrees with the original. The phase difference θ is due to the different velocities and, therefore, different equivalent air paths in the substance for the two kinds of vibrations. If the two indices are denoted by n_1 and n_2 and the thickness of material by t, the difference in equivalent air path is $(n_1 - n_2)t$. This amounts to a fraction of an oscillation given by

$$(n_1 - n_2)\frac{t}{\lambda}.$$

Therefore the angular phase difference is

$$\theta° = (n_1 - n_2)\frac{t}{\lambda} 360°,$$

and the plane of polarization is rotated through half this angle.

124. Magneto- and Electro-optics.—A number of interesting polarization effects which are very important from the electronic point of view are produced in strong electric and magnetic fields. The first of these to be discovered was the effect of a magnetic field on the optical properties of substances. Faraday found, in 1845, that there is a rotation of the plane of polarization when light passes through a substance in a magnetic field in the direction of the lines of force. The rotation increases in general with the index of refraction, so that it is very marked in heavy flint glass and in carbon disulphide. The angle is proportional to the intensity of the magnetic field and to the thickness of the substance and it reverses with the field. Some substances, however, are right-handed while others are left-handed in their rotation. According to Lorentz, the effect is due to the deflections of electrons and positive ions which are thrown into vibration by the passing light wave. It can be shown mathematically that their reaction on the light wave causes its plane of polarization to rotate.

Very thin films of paramagnetic substances like iron, nickel, and cobalt produce very large rotations in proportion to their thickness. There is, accordingly, some dependence of this effect on magnetic properties. In the same class belongs an effect observed by Kerr who reflected polarized light off the polished polepieces of an electromagnet and found a change in its polarization. Plane polarized light reflected by metals becomes elliptically polarized unless it vibrates in or at right angles to the plane of incidence. In these cases it remains plane polarized upon reflection when the metal is unmagnetized. When, however, it is magnetized, then, even in these cases, there is ellipticity produced on reflection. The ellipse is usually narrow and inclined to the original vibration so that the effect may often be regarded as a rotation of the plane of polarization.

Kerr has shown that glass becomes doubly refracting in strong electric fields. This effect is partly due to electrostriction, which is simply a distortion of the glass by the strong electric field, but there is also a residual effect which can be explained only on the basis of a direct effect of the field on the electrons. This is related to Stark's comparatively recent discovery that with a source in a strong electric field, the spectrum lines are separated into polarized components. A similar effect was discovered by

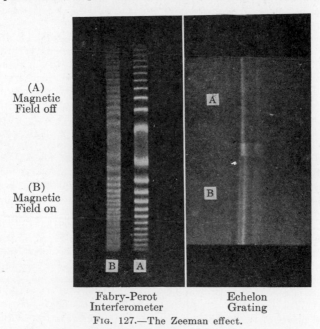

(A)
Magnetic
Field off

(B)
Magnetic
Field on

Fabry-Perot   Echelon
Interferometer   Grating
Fig. 127.—The Zeeman effect.

Zeeman in strong magnetic fields. The theories of these effects are still not completely satisfactory, but they are sure to have considerable bearing on the electromagnetic theory of light and the electron theory of matter.

Figure 127 shows the Zeeman effect with the 5,461 Ångström units mercury green line. The Fabry-Perot interferometer gives interference rings, a cross-section of which is shown at the left. The source was observed perpendicularly to the lines of force through a polarizer set to transmit vibrations at right angles to the field. The separation amounts to only 0.12 Ångström unit, the field strength being 3,500 gausses.

Problems

1. A plate of calcite 2 cm. thick, cut parallel to the optic axis, is placed over a mark on a microscope stage. What amount of adjustment is required to refocus the microscope for the ordinary and for the extraordinary ray? *Ans.* Ord. 0.794 cm.; Ext. 0.655 cm.

2. How does the intensity of light transmitted by two nicol prisms with their principal planes at an angle of 30° compare with the intensity when the nicols are parallel? *Ans. I* at 30° = 75 per cent of *I* at 0°.

3. (*a*) Suppose that the principal planes of two nicol prisms are at right angles and that a crystal plate is inserted between them with its principal plane at 30° with that of the first nicol. What are the relative amplitudes of the components of the extraordinary and ordinary rays which are transmitted by the second nicol prism? (*b*) What is the result if the principal plane of the second nicol is rotated 90°? *Ans.* (*a*) −1; (*b*) 3.

4. The principal indices of a mica plate are 1.5977 and 1.5936. What is the thickness of mica required to produce a quarter-wave plate for light of wave length 0.000055 cm.? *Ans.* 0.00334 cm.

5. A sugar solution rotates the plane of polarization 12° in a tube 20 cm. long. How many grams of sugar are there per cubic centimeter of solution if the specific rotatory power of the sugar is 66.6°? *Ans.* 0.0903 g. per cc.

6. A certain quartz plate rotates the plane of polarization of red light of wave length 0.000065 cm. through an angle of 90°. What wave length would be rotated through an angle of 270°? *Ans.* 0.00003754 cm.

7. A sugar solution rotates the plane of polarization 12^c. (*a*) What is the angular difference in phase between the right- and left-hand circularly polarized components of the transmitted light? (*b*) What is the difference between the indices of refraction of the solution for the two components if the length of tube for 12° rotation is 20 cm.? *Ans.* (*a*) 24°; (*b*) 0.00000018.

8. The principal plane of a crystal plate bisects the angle between the principal planes of the polarizer and analyzer which are at 60° with each other. What are the relative amplitudes of the two components transmitted by the analyzer? *Ans.* 3 to 1.

9. A crystal plate 0.1 mm. thick, having principal indices of n_e = 1.5590 and n_o = 1.5567 is placed in a polariscope. (*a*) What will be the difference in optical path for the transmitted rays? (*b*) What will be the difference in phase in degrees for light of 5,500 Å. U.? (1 Å. U. = 10^{-8} cm.) *Ans.* (*a*) 0.000023 cm.; (*b*) 150°.

10. How can one change the sense of rotation in circularly polarized light from clockwise to counterclockwise or *vice versa*? *Ans.* Rotate the quarter-wave plate through 90°.

CHAPTER XIII

RADIATION

125. Spectrum Analysis of Radiation.—When spectra of various sources are compared, it is found that they often differ greatly in appearance. The spectra fall into two general classes, called, respectively, *continuous* and *discontinuous* spectra according to whether there is or is not radiant energy corresponding to every wave length. To the first class belong the spectra of all solids and liquids emitting light by virtue of their high temperature alone, while to the other belong spectra of vapors and gases excited into luminescence by an electrical discharge or some other means. A carbon arc shows both types of spectra. The hot carbons give continuous spectra of which the negative is redder because of a lower temperature. The gases between the carbons give a discontinuous spectrum consisting of narrow lines emitted by the metallic impurities, and a set of fluted bands in the violet due to nitrogen. These bands give the arc its characteristic color. With a spectroscope of high resolving power they are found to consist of hundreds of fine lines very close together, so that in a single prism spectroscope they appear as fluted bands usually terminating sharply on one side (Fig. 128C). Discontinuous spectra are called either *band* or *line* spectra, according to the prominence or absence of such fine groups.

126. Infra-red and Ultra-violet Rays.—If spectra are examined visually, it appears that the wave lengths emitted always lie between 7,600 and 3,800 Ångström units (the Ångström unit is 10^{-8} centimeter). These are, respectively, the red and the violet limits of the visible spectrum and, also, the limits of the physical spectrum as known from the time of Newton until about a century later. Then Herschel showed, in 1800, that there were radiations with wave lengths longer than the eye could detect in practically any spectrum. These radiations are called infra-red rays, and they differ physically from visible light only in their wave length. They are best detected by means of sensitive detectors of the heat generated when these rays are absorbed.

Instruments for use in measuring infra-red wave lengths or for studying properties of materials for these rays must be specially constructed, because many ordinary substances do not transmit the waves when they are too long.   Thus glass, for example, does not transmit infra-red waves longer than 3 microns (a micron is a thousandth of a millimeter).   Quartz is somewhat better, for it is transparent to 6.5 microns and so it is often used.   The best materials are rock salt and sylvite (KCl).   These substances are transparent to 18 and to 22 microns, respectively.   Such prisms or lenses must be kept in a dry atmosphere to avoid tarnish of the polished faces by moisture.   Instead of lenses, however, it is

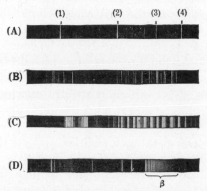

Fig. 128.—Line and band spectra.   (*A*) Spectrum of hydrogen.   Note first four lines of Balmer series.   (*B*) Spectrum of argon.   Compare this spectrum of a monatomic gas with (*C*).   (*C*) Spectrum of nitrogen.   Note bands characteristic of molecular spectra.   (*D*) Band at β partly resolved.

customary to use concave mirrors in the infra-red.   To detect the infra-red rays, one may use a bolometer or a thermopile as described in Art. 19.   These have been made so sensitive as to respond to a rise in temperature of a millionth of a degree. Using these or other detectors of the rays as "eyes," one can study the optical properties of materials in the infra-red.

Soon after the discovery of infra-red rays, Ritter and Wollaston found that a spectrum also contained wave lengths shorter than any the eye could detect.   These were called *ultra-violet* rays. These rays are usually not present in large enough quantity to use the heat-detection method on them.   Fortunately, they are very efficient in promoting certain chemical reactions.   Thus they affect a photographic plate.   They are sometimes called *actinic*, or *chemical*, rays.   This property is due to their short wave length and, consequently, high frequency, which is often high enough to expel electrons from atoms and thus start chemical processes. Physically they differ from visible light only in that their wave length is shorter.

Ordinary glass will transmit only ultra-violet rays having wave lengths longer than about 3,300 Ångström units. Hence, instruments designed for utilizing shorter ultra-violet rays must be constructed of special materials. Quartz is often used, for it is transparent enough down to 1,900 Ångström units. Fluorite is preferred for some work, because it transmits to 1,200 Ångström units.

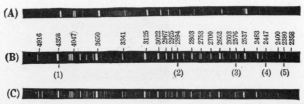

Fig. 129.—Spectra of mercury vapor. (*A*) Low voltage arc. Spectrum of neutral mercury atoms. Wave-length scale below. (*B*) Bombardment by 23-volt electrons. Wave lengths of some prominent arc lines are given in Ångström units. In the case of unresolved groups the shortest wave length is indicated. One of the many spectral series is shown. Compare with (*A*) and note appearance of some "spark" lines due to singly ionized mercury atoms. (*C*) Bombardment by 1,000-volt electrons. Compare with (*B*) and (*A*) and note appearance of many "spark" lines some of which are due to multiply ionized mercury atoms.

Ultra-violet rays with wave lengths between 2,900 and 3,100 have been found to promote health and even to cure some diseases which are difficult to treat in any other way. These rays are often referred to as the "vital rays." They are present in small amount in sunlight and in electric arcs and sparks when not enclosed by glass. The mercury arc in quartz is a particularly strong source of these rays (see Fig. 129*A*). Although ordinary window glass transmits ultra-violet rays down to 3,300 Ångström units, which comprise most of the ultra-violet energy in sunlight, still it does not transmit any of the vital rays. There have recently appeared several glasses of special chemical composition and also a number of glass substitutes to correct this defect. Some of these compare favorably with quartz in their transmission of the vital-ray wave lengths as may be seen in Fig. 130.

127. The Complete Spectrum.—The discovery of wave lengths of light, both longer and shorter than the eye could detect, led to many investigations which extended the limits of the spectrum farther and farther on both sides. While this was going on, Hertz discovered waves radiated by oscillating electrical circuits which had all the properties of light, such as interference, diffraction, polarization, and even had the same velocity as light in a vacuum, but their wave lengths were much longer than the longest infra-red rays.

The wave lengths of Hertzian waves may be measured by observing the nodes and loops of stationary waves produced

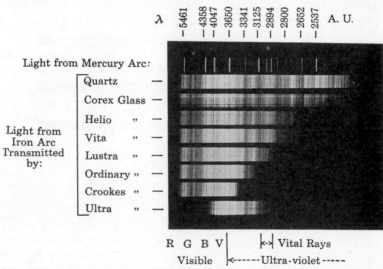

FIG. 130.—Transmissibility of various kinds of glass for ultra-violet light of various wave length.

when they travel along a wire and are reflected back. In the case of longer waves such as are used in radiocasting, the wave lengths are more easily determined by calculation from the values of the inductance and capacity of resonating circuits.

Not long after Hertz's discovery, Roentgen found, in 1895, another kind of radiation which was later shown to be similar to light, differing only in that its wave length is shorter even than that of ultra-violet light. The rays discovered by Roentgen are called X-rays, and their characteristic peculiarity is that they pass through many materials which are opaque to visible light. This is especially true if the rays have a very short wave length. Such rays are said to be "hard." The longer the wave length, the "softer" the radiation becomes, and the more easily it is absorbed. In fact, X-rays may be so soft as not to pass through any material. Such X-rays have a still shorter wave length than ultra-violet light.

X-rays are emitted whenever electrons having a high velocity strike a metallic target. In the modern tubes the electrons are obtained by heating a filament to incandescence. A high voltage is applied between the filament and a metallic target, such that the electrons are driven against the target at high speed. The higher the voltage and, therefore, the velocity, the shorter the wave length and the greater the hardness of the rays.

Wave lengths of X-rays are measured by using a crystal as a diffraction grating. The spectrometer on which it is mounted is

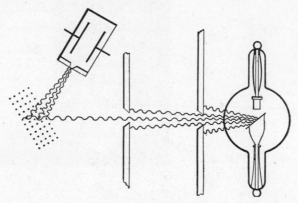

Fig. 131.—X-ray diffraction.

specially constructed for use with X-rays. Several lead slits are used as a collimator to give a definite ray. This ray is diffracted, and there will be several places (orders) where the wavelets will arrive in the same phase and reenforce each other. Since these positions depend on the wave length, there are one or more spectra produced. These are not visible directly, of course, but can be made so by means of a fluorescent screen, by photography, or by an ionization chamber. The last is a metal enclosure with a slit in front of it, and is mounted like the telescope of an ordinary spectrometer. Inside it has two electrodes between which a current passes when the gas is ionized. The amount of ionization produced by any particular wave length entering the chamber depends on the intensity of the rays and is measured by means of an electroscope. The general arrangement is shown in Fig. 131. For a deep grating like a crystal, other conditions hold for maxima than for a flat diffraction grating, because in this case the effects from all planes must be in phase. This condition necessitates that the crystal setting be as for reflection, namely, angles of incidence and reflection being equal, and in addition the angle itself must be such that wavelets from successive planes differ in phase by an integral number of wave lengths. This gives a perfectly definite setting for both the crystal and the ionization chamber for every wave length. Thus, only one wave length is registered for each crystal setting and this is found in a definite direction. To get the entire spectrum, the crystal must be rotated; this is usually

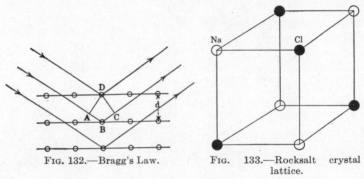

Fig. 132.—Bragg's Law.

Fig. 133.—Rocksalt crystal lattice.

done by a motor. A. W. Hull has, however, developed a method using powdered crystal which does not require rotation. The powder contains tiny crystals at all angles, of which only those turned just right will reflect any given spectrum line. Between themselves they produce the entire spectrum. If we let d represent the distance between atomic planes and θ the angle between the planes and a line in the direction of some diffraction maximum, the wave length producing this maximum is given by Bragg's formula

$$m\lambda = 2d \sin \theta,$$

where m is an integer giving the order of the spectrum.

In order to derive this equation, consider a set of atomic planes at distances d from each other, as in Fig. 132. The wavelets reflected at the same angle from any two adjacent planes will have a difference in path given by ABC in the figure, where AD and CD are perpendicular to the rays. When ABC is any integral multiple of a wave length, the wavelets will all be in the same phase and the reflection will be strong if there are enough atomic planes. At other angles the reflection will be exceedingly weak. The intensity maxima will accordingly be found in directions given by

$$m\lambda = ABC = 2AB = 2d \sin \theta,$$

where θ is the angle between the atomic planes and the incident or diffracted rays.

The value of the lattice constant d is calculated in the following way. Rocksalt is known to be a cubic crystal and the diffraction experiments indicate that the atoms are arranged as shown in Fig. 133. The length of the side of this cube is the quantity d, and the volume is therefore d^3. Let the density of rocksalt be ρ. The mass of the unit cube is then $d^3\rho$. This mass can also be calculated from the number and masses of the atoms in each cell. Each atom is shared by eight cells so that there is only half of an NaCl molecule per cell. The molecular weight of NaCl is 58.46 and the number of molecules in a gram molecule is known to be 60.61×10^{22} from Faraday's constant of electrolysis (charge per univalent gram molecule) and the charge per electron. Thus the mass of an NaCl molecule is 9.64×10^{-23} gram and therefore the mass of a unit cell in the crystal is 4.82×10^{-23} gram. This is equal to $d^3\rho$, where ρ has the value 2.1632. Thus it is found that

$$d = 2.814 \text{ Angström units.}$$

In a similar manner it is found that for calcite

$$d = 3.029 \text{ Angström units.}$$

Recently it has been possible to verify these values by measurement of the wave length of X-rays by means of ruled gratings. Such experiments were successful only after it was learned that it is possible to obtain total reflection of X-rays if the glancing angle is small enough. This follows as a consequence of the index of refraction being less than one. (By only 1×10^{-6}!) In fact, even prism spectrograms of the softer X-rays have been obtained by Siegbahn and his associates. The wave length of X-rays measured in terms of the measurable rulings on the grating lead to a lattice constant of calcite or rocksalt which is only slightly greater than the above values.

A study of X-ray emission has shown that there is a simple relation between voltage and wave length. Thus it is found that the shortest wave length emitted is given by the formula

$$\lambda_{min} = \frac{12.34}{V},$$

in which the wave length is in Ångström units and the voltage in kilovolts. It is interesting that a beam of X-rays will eject electrons with a velocity equal to that required to produce the rays. The velocity may be measured by applying a retarding potential to a grid through which the electrons are passing, until the potential is high enough to stop them. The retarding potential needed will be found related to the wave length by the formula given above, so that this method is sometimes used to measure wave lengths, particularly of soft X-rays. It was in this way that the gap which long existed between X-rays and ultra-violet light was first bridged. Since these very soft X-rays are so easily absorbed by everything, including air, the apparatus must be enclosed in an evacuated container.

For a number of years there was also an unexplored gap in the spectrum between the longest infra-red rays and the shortest Hertzian rays. In 1923, this gap was closed by the work of Nichols and Tear in which they used extraordinarily delicate electrical oscillators and resonators as well as a specially designed interferometer and radiometer. Both methods were successfully used in this region of the spectrum.

To this list of electromagnetic radiations, extending in wave length from the enormously big to the minutely small, must be added two more radiations. First of all, it has been shown that many radioactive substances radiate a very penetrating kind of X-ray which has been called the *gamma ray*. Alpha and beta rays consist of charged particles and hence are excluded from this list. The shorter of the gamma ray wave lengths are so small that even crystals are too coarse to enable more than a mere estimate of their wave length to be made. Moreover, the electrons liberated by these rays possess so high a velocity that it is impossible to apply a field high enough to stop them and obtain the wave length in this way. But the paths of these high-speed electrons can be deflected by means of a magnetic field, and the radius of curvature of their path can be measured. From these data, their velocity and, hence, the voltage that would be able to stop them may be calculated. From this result and the formula given on a preceding page, the wave length can be found.

Finally, another type of radiation having a wave length still shorter than the gamma ray has been recently found. These are called *cosmic rays* because they seem to come from interstellar space. They have an enormous penetrating power, being able to pass through 6 feet of lead. The amount of this radiation is very small. From their penetrating power and the formula which has been found to relate this to wave length in the X-ray and gamma ray regions, it is estimated that their wave lengths are about as much shorter than X-rays as the wave lengths of X-rays are shorter than visible light.

Below is a table giving the names and wave-length limits of different regions of the complete electromagnetic spectrum as

TABLE X.—COMPLETE SPECTRUM OF ELECTROMAGNETIC RADIATIONS

Name	Wave-length range	Wave length measured by
Cosmic rays......	0.0004 to 0.00067 Ångström unit	Penetrating power
Gamma rays......	0.00557 to 1.0 Ångström unit	Magnetic deflection of secondary β-rays
X-rays..........	0.012 to 10.0 Ångström units	Crystal diffraction
Ultra-soft X-rays	10.0 to 100 Ångström units	Grating in vacuo
Far ultra-violet...	100 to 1,800 Ångström units	Grating in vacuo
Near ultra-violet..	1,800 to 3,800 Ångström units	Grating, etc.
Visible..........	3,800 to 7,600 Ångström units	Grating, etc.
Near infra-red....	0.76 to 22.5 microns	Grating, etc.
Far infra-red......	22.5 to 100 microns	Interferometer
Ultra-short Hertzian waves......	0.1 to 1.8 millimeters	Interferometer or delicate resonator
Hertzian waves...	1.8 to 300 millimeters	Hertzian resonator or waves on wires
Radio waves......	0.3 to 30,000 meters	Resonating circuit

The range of wave lengths of all known electromagnetic radiations is from 0.0004 to 300,000,000,000,000 + Ångström units.

known at present. It must be kept in mind that there are no sharp boundaries between the different regions, the wave lengths being merely given to indicate the order of magnitude of what are commonly assumed to be boundaries. The values are often determined by the limiting wave length conveniently attainable with some particular kind of apparatus. When these wave lengths are small fractions of a millimeter, it is convenient to express them in smaller units such as the micron, millimicron, or Ångström unit. These are, respectively, equal to 10^{-3}, 10^{-6}, and 10^{-7} of a millimeter.

128. Thermal Radiation.—When a solid body is heated to higher and higher temperatures in a dark room, it first radiates only infra-red rays, until at about 500°C. a faint dull-red glow becomes visible. This increases in brightness and becomes yellow as the temperature rises, finally becoming a dazzling white above the temperature of 1800°C. As the temperature increases, it is apparent that the body emits more radiant energy as a whole, but especially does it radiate more of the shorter wave lengths so that its color shifts toward the blue. A spectrum analysis of the radiation confirms this. The spectrum is found continuous and with a definite intensity of radiation at each wave length. Intensity of radiation at a wave length is defined as the radiant energy per unit area, per unit time, per unit wave-length interval at that particular wave length. It can be measured by means of a thermopile, bolometer, or other form of radiometer. If these intensities are plotted as ordinates against the wave lengths as abscissas, a smooth curve is obtained for each temperature. The curves approach zero for very short and for very long waves, there being a maximum intensity for some intermediate wave length. A comparison of curves for higher temperatures shows that they are above those for lower temperatures at all wave lengths and that their maxima come at shorter wave lengths.

This is shown by the curves given in Fig. 134, which illustrate the results obtained by Lummer and Pringsheim. The visible region lies between the vertical lines V and R. The energy at all wave lengths is seen to increase with temperature, but at the short waves it increases faster. As is very evident, most of the energy lies in the infra red for the temperatures shown. The ratio of luminous to non-luminous radiant energy equals the ratio of the area under the curves between V and R to the total area. This ratio is larger for higher temperatures up to 6000°C. abs. (Appendix, Table VIII). Most of the common sources of light are luminous solely because of their high temperature. Their efficiency is usually very low. The incandescent Mazda lamps are only 5 per cent efficient. Nitrogen-filled lamps are somewhat better, because their filaments can be operated at a higher temperature.

129. The Radiation Laws.—The distribution of energy among the wave lengths usually depends on both the temperature and the nature of the substance which is heated. In the very important case of a uniformly heated enclosure, however, it is found that the radiation escaping through a small opening depends only on the temperature and not at all on the nature of the walls. This is the principle of the "black body" first stated definitely by Kirchhoff. He showed that the ratio of the emissive power e_λ, *i.e.*, the energy radiated per unit area per unit time, to the absorptive power a_λ, at any particular wave length, λ, is a constant for all surfaces at the same temperature. Thus

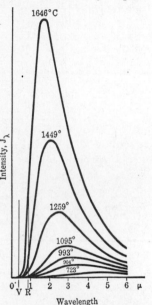

FIG. 134.—Radiation by a black body.

$$\frac{e_\lambda}{a_\lambda} = J_\lambda,$$

where J_λ is a constant that depends only on temperature and wave length and is the same for all substances. If the body is so constructed that $a_\lambda = 1$, then its emissive power is equal to J_λ. It can never exceed this if the radiation is due solely to high temperature, because a_λ cannot be greater than 1. Thus a perfect absorber or so-called "black body" has the highest possible emissivity for radiations produced by heat.

It is possible to deduce many facts about the radiation of a black body by the mathematical processes of thermodynamics. In this way Boltzmann was able to prove the law suggested by Stefan, that the total energy J emitted by a black body is proportional to the fourth power of the absolute temperature T. Thus

$$J = cT^4,$$

where c is a constant found experimentally to be 5.45×10^{-12}

watt per square centimeter per degree to the fourth power. This quantity J is proportional to the areas under the curves in Fig. 134 and shows how rapidly they increase with temperature.

Similarly, Wien deduced the relation between the wave length of the maximum radiation λ_m and the absolute temperature. The relation is simply

$$\lambda_m T = b,$$

where b is a constant found to be 0.2911 centimeter-degree. This law has been used to estimate the temperature of the sun and of other celestial bodies. A radiometric analysis of sunlight gives $\lambda_m = 0.000047$ centimeter, so that the temperature must be about 6190°abs. or 5920°C. The temperatures of the blue stars and nebulae giving continuous spectra must sometimes be as high as 20,000°C. if they radiate because of temperature alone.

The formula for the actual distribution of energy among the various wave lengths at any temperature is not so easy to derive as those given above. There have been several attempts to develop one on purely theoretical grounds. The best of these is that derived by Max Planck in 1900. In his derivation it is of interest to note that Planck was forced to make the assumption that light energy exists in chunks, "quanta," or atoms of energy. The magnitude of a quantum is $h\nu$ where ν is the frequency, and h is called Planck's constant and is equal to 6.55×10^{-27} erg-second. He was forced to make this step in order to come anywhere near the correct result, and when he did make it the result was perfect so far as modern measurements can show. The most surprising thing is that his idea of quanta has been since confirmed and applied with remarkable success in various fields, such as the theory of specific heats, especially, at low temperatures, fluorescence, ionization, spectral series, X-rays, and related subjects. The distribution law of Planck is

$$J_\lambda = c_1 \lambda^{-5} \left(e^{\frac{c_2}{\lambda T}} - 1 \right)^{-1},$$

where c_1 is equal to 3.703×10^{-12} watt per square centimeter per unit wave-length interval, and c_2 is 1.4330 centimeter-degrees. In the visible region it happens to turn out that the first term in the parenthesis is over 10,000, so that the 1 can be practically neglected. We can then write for the visible region, approximately,

$$J_\lambda = c_1\lambda^{-5}e^{-\frac{c_2}{\lambda T}}.$$

This is the law originally derived by Wien on somewhat faulty hypotheses. It fails in the infra-red but works very satisfactorily for the visible and the ultra-violet regions.

130. Radiation and Optical Pyrometry.—For measuring temperatures up to 1200°C., thermocouples of the common base metals are very convenient. The alloys used have various trade names such as constantan, nichrome, chromel, alumel, etc. For higher temperatures, the couples, if used, must be of refractory metals, such as platinum, rhodium, iridium, and their alloys. Even these are only good to about 1750°C., the melting point of platinum. For still higher temperatures, only radiation means can be employed. Often these are preferable between 1000 and 1750°C. as well.

The so-called radiation pyrometers measure the intensity of the total radiation J from a uniformly heated enclosure in a furnace, or often the furnace itself. The heating of a sensitive thermopile on to which the radiation is focused is measured electrically. The instrument is calibrated by observing the melting points of some metals which have been measured by means of a standard gas thermometer.

Optical pyrometers are instruments for measuring temperatures by optical observation. They employ some kind of photometric process to measure the intensity J_λ at some particular wave length which is usually in the red part of the spectrum. Red is chosen because it is radiated at lower temperatures. This instrument must also be calibrated by the method mentioned above. The observations are correct only when the light comes from a black body.

131. Luminescence.—When light is radiated by some process in which high temperature is not the main consideration, the light is said to be due to luminescence. Popularly, such radiation is referred to as "cold light." The spectrum of luminescent radiation differs from that of thermal radiation in that it is always discontinuous, while the latter consists of a single broad continuous band having the general features described above. The spectrum of a luminescing source sometimes consists of a group of bands, sometimes of narrow lines, and, occasionally, of combinations of the two (Fig. 128). The wave lengths of the bands or lines are characteristic of the material used. It has been proved that band spectra are produced by radiating molecules, while line spectra are due to single atoms. This is shown by the fact that bands disappear when the molecules are dissociated. Very often bands can be resolved into many fine lines when a spectroscope of sufficient resolving power is used. This is the case when the radiation comes from a gas at low pressure. In the case of light from liquids and solids the fine structure of the bands is blurred together and cannot be resolved.

Luminescence may be excited in various ways but ultimately these are the same in that they all involve a disturbance of the

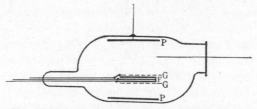

FIG. 135.—Tube for study of electroluminescence.

natural energy states of electrons. Luminescence may be excited: (1) by the striking of atoms by electrons (and perhaps positive ions), when these are set in motion by an electric field; (2) by radiation from other atoms; (3) by some chemical reactions; and (4) by mechanical means. Of greatest interest perhaps is the first method, for in this class belongs the radiation emitted by vapors and gases in electric arcs and sparks. The second group includes radiation by fluorescence and phosphorescence. The third is illustrated by the glow of phosphorus, or of fireflies. In the fourth group belongs the glow observed when some crystals are rubbed or crushed in a perfectly dark room.

132. Electroluminescence.—A method of investigation which has given much information as to the emission of light in general is the study of the luminescence excited by electron impact at different electron speeds. The general method of procedure is to use a tube very similar to radio vacuum tubes, but containing a gas at low pressure (Fig. 135). Electrons liberated by heating a filament F to incandescence are accelerated by applying to the grid G a definite potential V above that of the filament. The grid should be close to the filament so that the likelihood of a collision with gas molecules or atoms between the two is small. In this way, the electrons passing through the openings of the grid have a kinetic energy equal to eV, where e represents the electronic charge of 4.77×10^{-10} electrostatic unit, and V is the potential of the grid with respect to the filament expressed in absolute electrostatic units, or, in other words, $V =$ volts divided by 300. The velocity v of the electrons is then given by

$$\frac{1}{2}mv^2 = eV,$$

in which m is the mass of an electron and is equal to 9.00×10^{-28} gram. The electrons strike the gas molecules and cause them to radiate. Spectra of mercury vapor obtained in this way are shown in Fig. 129B and C. By varying the potential V while examining the light spectroscopically, it is found that for each spectrum line or group of lines there is a definite minimum energy, *i.e.*, velocity, the electrons must have before that line appears. The corresponding grid potentials are called radiation potentials. Their values depend on the structure of the molecules or atoms in the tube, and will be discussed on page 200.

133. Photoluminescence.—Sometimes radiation is absorbed by a substance and then re-emitted as light, usually of longer wave length. This is known as photoluminescence. If the re-emission ceases as soon as the exciting light is cut off, the process is called *fluorescence*. If it persists for some time after, it is called *phosphorescence*. This may persist for days, but there are many phosphorescent compounds which luminesce only for very short times, so that there is no true boundary between the two effects.

The photoluminescence of a substance is usually easy to detect when excited by ultra-violet light, since then some of the secondary radiations are usually visible, being of a longer wave length than the primary light. A change in color is really the most distinguishing feature even when visible light is used, and especially when observations are made in the colors of a spectrum. Ordinary non-luminescent substances in the spectral colors have exactly the same hue as that of the light falling on them. If, however, the substance is luminescent, it has its own characteristic luminescent color. Still another distinction is derived from the fact that a beam of light passing through a non-luminescing solution will not be visible from the side if there are no suspended particles. If, however, the solution is luminescent, there will be much light scattered to the side due to re-radiation and the solution will appear cloudy, although in light of longer wave length it will appear perfectly clear. This scattering is, in fact, the only way one can detect photoluminescence when it happens that the secondary radiation has the same wave length as that which excites it. This has been observed in many vapors. For example, when sodium vapor is illuminated by sodium light, it will re-radiate the same light in all directions. Such luminescence is called *resonance radiation*.

Some fluorescing substances are sulphate of quinine, fluorspar, coal oil, fluorescein, chlorophyll, eosine, rhodamin, and iodine. The exciting light must be contained in a certain definite band of wave lengths in order to excite fluorescence. The spectrum of the secondary radiation also consists of a band which may overlap the effective exciting region but is always, on the average, of longer wave length. Stokes at one time stated that the emitted light is always of a longer wave length than the exciting light, but this is not exactly true, for the overlapping of the two wave-length regions allows the possibility of having shorter waves sometimes emitted.

Fluorescence is caused by the disturbance of electron orbits by the exciting light. The radiation is emitted during the return to the normal state.

Phosphorescence seems similar to fluorescence in everything except time of duration. It is especially prominent in the sulphides of calcium, strontium, and barium. Slight amounts of impurities must be present to produce phosphorescence. The process probably involves changes in structure of complex chemical compounds and the formation of others. The recombination tending toward the original state takes place slowly with emission of light. There are many substances which phosphoresce feebly at ordinary temperatures but glow strongly when cooled in liquid air. Examples of these are gelatin, horn, egg shells, and paper.

134. Spectral Series.—Spectrum lines usually appear to be distributed throughout the spectrum in a chaotic manner; but, nevertheless, in every case, it is possible to find series of lines, the frequencies of which may be represented by some definite formula. Such a series of lines is called a *spectral series*. For example, in the spectrum of atomic hydrogen there is found a series, called the Balmer series (Fig. 128*A*), in which the frequencies can be represented by the formula

$$\nu = R\left[\frac{1}{2^2} - \frac{1}{m^2}\right], \text{with } m = 3, 4, 5, \text{etc.},$$

in which R is a constant known as Rydberg's constant and has the value 3.29034×10^{15}. When R is put equal to 109,677.7, the same formula gives the wave numbers of the spectrum lines, that is, the number of waves per centimeter. Only the first three lines of this series can be seen visually, because the others are in the ultra-violet. While studying the spectrum in the far ultra-violet, Lyman found a new series represented by a formula just like the above but with the 2^2 in the denominator of the first fraction replaced by 1. The values of m start at 2 in this case. Later, Paschen discovered another series, this time in the infra-red, which followed the same formula except that a 3^2 appeared in the first term. Evidently something fundamental in regard to the mechanism of the hydrogen atom is hereby disclosed.

Spectral series also exist in the spectra of other elements, (Fig. 129*B*), but the frequencies do not follow quite so simple a formula. The formula usually followed is one known as the Rydberg formula and is written as follows

$$\nu = R'\left[\frac{1}{(m_1 + a_1)^2} - \frac{1}{(m_2 + a_2)^2}\right].$$

In this formula m_1 and m_2 take on integral values, while a_1 and a_2 are decimals to be added to them. For any series, m_1, a_1, and a_2 take on definite values, while m_2 varies by steps of unity starting with the next integer greater than m_1. R' has a definite value for each element. It is readily seen that the series in hydrogen are also represented by this formula but that the values of a_1 and a_2 happen to be negligible in this case.

Band spectra also possess regularities in form and position. Deslandres has shown that the fine-line constituents may be represented by the formula

$$\nu = A \pm 2Bm + Cm^2,$$

where A, B, and C are constants for any single band, and m is a positive integer; 0, 1, 2, 3, etc.

This regularity of spacing of lines in both the line and band spectra reminds one of the regularity of the overtones of a tuning fork, but it is not nearly so simple. It is, of course, a question, respectively, of atomic and molecular structure, and this is no simple thing, except possibly in the case of hydrogen. The problem of deducing atomic structure from spectrum lines has attracted very many physicists. The present theory is an outgrowth of the pioneer work of Niels Bohr, at Copenhagen, and of Arnold Sommerfeld, at Munich.

135. Atomic Structure.—It was Rutherford who pointed out that atoms consist of positive nuclei surrounded by electrons in sufficient number to neutralize the positive charge, and that as one passes from the lightest atom, hydrogen, to the heaviest, uranium, the nuclear charges and, therefore, surrounding electrons increase in number from 1 to 92. The charge on the nucleus expressed in electron units is called the *atomic number* of the element and is roughly equal to half of the atomic weight for the lighter elements (see Table IX, in the Appendix). The electrons around the nucleus are in groups or "shells" in conformity with the periodic table (see Table X, in the Appendix). The electrons in the outermost shell are the most loosely bound and are called the valence electrons. The most easily excited radiation comes from these electrons.

To explain spectral series, Bohr assumes that the electrons all revolve around the nucleus in certain definite orbits. Besides the orbits which are occupied by the electrons, there are a number of virtual orbits in which a valence electron may temporarily revolve. This occurs when the atom has been excited by one of the various methods mentioned in a preceding paragraph. When the electron returns to its normal orbit, light is radiated. This return may take place in steps through other virtual orbits. Each step corresponds to a spectrum line, the frequency of which is equal to the difference between the energies of the initial and the final orbits divided by Planck's constant. Steps in which the final orbit is the same result in lines belonging to the same spectral series. The theory can be made quantitative in the case of the hydrogen atom. In all other cases, the electrodynamical problem of the orbits becomes too difficult to solve. However, see Article 136.

The hydrogen atom consists of a nucleus and a single electron. In the normal state, the electron is in some orbit close to the nucleus, but when the atom is excited, the electron will, for a short time, occupy some orbit farther away. Bohr assumes that only certain definite orbits are possible, and that these are determined by the angular momenta being equal to integral multiples of $h/2\pi$, where h is the well-known Planck's constant, which is equal to 6.55×10^{-27} erg-second. Thus, an electron in the first orbit (nearest the nucleus) would have an angular momentum of $h/2\pi$; in the second, $2h/2\pi$, and in the mth, $mh/2\pi$. The energy of the atom depends on the orbit occupied by the electron and can be calculated from the above with the use of electrodynamics. It is found that if the electron is in the mth orbit the energy is $-hR/m^2$, where R represents an algebraic expression involving the charge and mass of an electron and the value of Planck's constant. When the numerical values are substituted, it is found that R comes out equal to 3.29034×10^{15}, which is Rydberg's constant.

Consider now two orbits represented by the "quantum numbers" m_1 and m_2, of which the second is the larger. The energy of the atom when the electron is in the m_1 orbit is given by $W_1 = -hR/m_1^2$, while when the electron is in the m_2 orbit the energy is $W_2 = -hR/m_2^2$. The negative sign comes from the definition of energy as the ability to do work, coupled with the choice of the standard state or "zero" of energy as the complete removal of the electron. Since the electron and nucleus have opposite charges, this removal requires work instead of giving any, and hence the ability to do work is zero or less. It will be observed that, when the electron is in an orbit farther from the nucleus, the energy is greater than when it is nearer. Thus, there is a decrease in the energy of the atom when the electron passes to an orbit nearer to the nucleus. Bohr assumes that this energy is emitted as a single quantum, $h\nu$, of radiation. The frequency is then given by the so-called *Bohr frequency condition:*

$$\nu = \frac{(W_2 - W_1)}{h},$$

or

$$\nu = R\left[\frac{1}{m_1^2} - \frac{1}{m_2^2}\right].$$

If the final orbit is the nearest to the nucleus, $m_1 = 1$, and the frequencies of the Lyman series are obtained on giving m_2 various

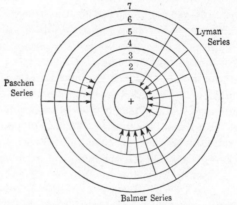

FIG. 136.—Bohr's theory of the hydrogen spectrum.

integral values. The Balmer series, on the other hand, is emitted when the final orbit is the second from the nucleus, $m_1 = 2$. Figure 136 shows diagrammatically the production of the hydrogen spectrum. Bohr's theory does not attempt to explain the act of radiation except in terms of energy changes.

Bohr's theory is remarkable not only in its giving the correct formula for spectral series and the relations between different series, but also in its derivation of R in terms of quantities, such as the charge and mass of an electron, which are measured by methods entirely foreign to spectroscopy. This is a very fine confirmation of the essentials of Bohr's theory. Actually, however, there are some modifications necessary even for hydrogen, since it is observed that the spectrum lines are not single but are very close multiplets. These are so fine that they can be seen only in the best spectroscopes, but still they show that Bohr's theory as it stands is too simple to account for the facts. Sommerfeld introduced the idea of elliptical as well as circular orbits and calculated the energies using Einstein's theory of relativity, and thus was able partly to account for the fine structure. A theory of the complete fine structure followed the introduction of the idea of the spinning electron by Uhlenbeck and Goudsmit in 1926. Energy changes due to reversals of electron spin led to the needed modification in the energy-level scheme. Further refinements in the theory, particularly in regard to the calculation of the intensities of the spectral lines as well as their wave lengths, has finally led to three complete re-formulations of the mathematical theory along apparently entirely different lines. These recent developments are principally the work of Heisenberg, Schroedinger, and Dirac, respectively.

136. Spectral Terms and Energy Levels.—It will be observed that spectral series formulas are always differences of two terms A and B, of which the first is constant for any one series, and the other takes on successive values which decrease toward zero. Thus we always have

$$\nu = A - B.$$

Now, Bohr's theory indicates that A is proportional to the energy of the atom in the excited state of lesser energy (*i.e.*, larger negative) and B is proportional to the energy when the electron is farther from the nucleus. The constant of proportionality is $-h$ or -6.55×10^{-27} when ν is the frequency, while it has the value $-hc$ or -1.965×10^{-16} when ν is in wave-number units. The values of A and B cannot be calculated theoretically in cases other than that of hydrogen, but their values can always be found experimentally by a study of spectral series. They are called *spectral terms* and have been determined for many atoms. According to Bohr's theory, they give the values of the energy of the atom in various excited states when multiplied by the factors given above. Thus, even when the actual orbits of the electrons are unknown, one can still obtain the energy values. These are often represented by a diagram such as Fig.

137, which is for mercury vapor. The horizontal lines designate the various energy levels or spectral terms. It is customary to arrange the spectral terms in a downward increasing sequence. Since the energy is obtained by multiplying by a negative quantity, the energies really decrease downward. Hence emission corresponds to downward transitions on such a diagram. Some of these are indicated with the resulting wave lengths.

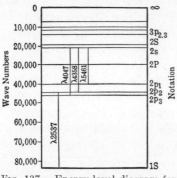

FIG. 137.—Energy-level diagram for mercury.

137. Radiation Potentials.—It is now possible to indicate the significance of the radiation potentials defined in a preceding paragraph. In order to cause the appearance of any given spectrum line, there is always some particular energy level which must be reached before the downward transition resulting in that line can take place. In case the luminescence is excited by electron impact, the electron must have at least enough energy to contribute to the atom in order to lift it from its normal state to that higher energy level. This depends on the accelerating potential used, since $\frac{1}{2}mv^2 = eV$, as explained in the paragraph on electroluminescence.

If the entire energy of the impinging electron is given to the atom, the maximum frequency or minimum wave length radiated will be given by the transition which radiates the entire added energy in one step, *i.e.*, in a single quantum. Hence,

$$h\nu_{max} = eV,$$

and since $\nu_{max} = c/\lambda_{min}$ it is found that

$$\lambda_{min} = \frac{hc}{eV}.$$

The units to be used in this formula are the centimeter-gram-second units, in which $c = 3 \times 10^{10}$ centimeters per second; $h = 6.55 \times 10^{-27}$ erg-second; $e = 4.77 \times 10^{-10}$ electrostatic unit; V = volts/300; and λ is in centimeters. Substituting these values, it is found that

$$\lambda_{min} = \frac{12,340}{V},$$

where V is expressed in volts, and λ is in Ångström units.

In order to obtain all the lines which the neutral atom can emit, the potential V must be high enough so that the valence electron can be knocked to the outermost orbit, which practically means temporary ionization of the atom. The spectrum obtained in such a case is called the "arc" spectrum of the substance. Numerical values of the ionization potentials for the chemical elements are given on page 241.

Still other lines appear when the orbits of an ionized atom are disturbed. These require a higher potential and are called "spark" lines (see Fig. 129B and C). Their emission is indicated on an entirely new energy-level diagram, which is, if the atom is singly ionized, similar to that for the arc spectrum of the atom with the next lower atomic number, except that the lines are displaced to shorter wave lengths.

138. Emission of X-rays.—Whereas "optical spectra" are emitted by the changes in the orbit of the outermost or valence electron, X-ray spectra, on the other hand, are emitted by changes in the orbits which are closer to the nucleus. In the normal state, these orbits are all occupied by electrons to saturation (Appendix, Table X), so there can be no transfers of electrons between orbits. To cause the emission of X-rays one of these more tightly held electrons must first be removed. In order to do this, the impinging electron must have an energy at least equal to that of the electron it removes. The resulting gap in the structure of the atom is filled by some other electron and this is followed by other rearrangements in the outer orbits. Each transition results in some X-ray spectrum line.

Spectral series also occur in X-ray emission, each series, as before, consisting of lines corresponding to the same final orbit. If the final orbit is one of the pair of orbits which make up the electron shell closest to the nucleus, the series is called the K series (Fig. 138) . If it is one of the next group of eight, the series is the L series; and so on. It requires the highest voltage to remove a K electron and thus to excite the K series. The voltage must be high enough so that the energy eV of the impinging electron must be at least equal to the energy in a quantum corresponding to the spectrum line of highest frequency; in other words, we must have $eV = h\nu_{max}$. This leads again to the formula

$$V = \frac{12.34}{\lambda_{min}},$$

where V is the potential across the X-ray tube in kilovolts, and λ_{min} is the shortest wave length radiated in Ångström units.

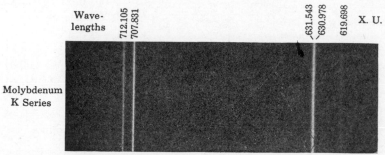

Fig. 138.—Characteristic K series X-ray emission from a molybdenum target.

For example, the wave length of the shortest line in the K series of tungsten is 0.1790 Ångström unit; hence the voltage needed is close to 69,000 volts. To obtain the complete L series of tungsten, one needs only 12,000 volts, since the shortest wave length is 1.044 Ångström units.

The K and L series have longer wave lengths when elements of lower atomic number are used as targets. Hence they are easier to excite but are not so penetrating. Moseley has shown that if one takes the square roots of the frequencies of corresponding lines in the spectra of various elements, it will be found that they are proportional to the atomic numbers. This regular variation in the X-ray spectra of different elements is illustrated in Fig. 139.

The simplicity and regularity of X-ray spectra make them very useful in performing chemical analyses. The usual procedure is to photograph the K (or L) series of the mixture to be analyzed along with the spectra of known elements with atomic numbers near those of the unknowns to be searched for. Then by interpolation (or extrapolation), using Moseley's law, one can determine the exact positions of the spectrum lines of the unknown with respect to the known lines. The presence of lines in the predicted locations indicates the presence of the corresponding elements. The scarcity of lines in the X-ray spectra makes this method much more unambiguous than the optical-spectrum method.

The above procedure is especially valuable in the search for elements, the spectra of which have not been observed previously.

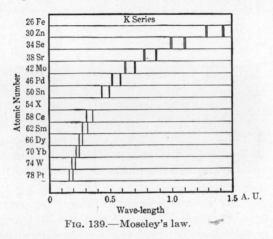

FIG. 139.—Moseley's law.

In fact the element itself may be one which has never been isolated. The spectra of such elements can be accurately predicted by Moseley's law. A few years ago there were many gaps in the periodic table which suggested possible undiscovered elements. By means of X-ray studies of the spectra of ores of elements in the same column of the periodic table, several of these have been identified. These are: hafnium, atomic number 72, discovered by Coster and Hevesy in 1923; rhenium, 75, and masurium, 43, both discovered by Noddack, Tacke, and Berg in 1925; and illinium, 61, discovered by Harris, Yntema, and Hopkins in 1926.

In addition to the X-ray line spectra there is always a continuous spectrum superposed. This spectrum appears at a lower voltage and is thought to be due to the radiation emitted by the impinging electrons themselves when they are suddenly stopped by the target. The resulting radiation is referred to as *general* X-radiation, while the line spectra are said to consist of *characteristic* X-rays because they are characteristic of the metal of which the target is made. These two kinds of radiation are illustrated by Fig. 140, which shows a graphical plot of the spectrum of tungsten as observed by the use of an ionization

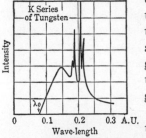

chamber. The ordinates are proportional to the intensities of the rays for the wave lengths which are plotted as abscissas. The short wave limit of the general radiation and the voltage on the tube are related by the same formula as given above.

The hardest characteristic rays are those of uranium which have a wave

FIG. 140.—Character- length of 107 X-ray units[1] and require
istic and general X-rays 115 kilovolts for their excitation.
superposed.

Needless to say, these are very penetrating. They can pass through about ⅛ inch of lead, or about 1 inch of steel, with appreciable intensity. It is, however, possible to obtain much harder *general* radiation by using higher differences in potential. The shortest wave length obtainable by commercial apparatus is at present 41 X-ray units[1] which is obtained at 300 kilovolts. Such rays will penetrate 4½ inches of steel and are therefore of value in examination of castings for internal flaws. In this machine age there are occasions when a flaw may result in a very serious accident, let alone the waste in machining a casting which may later have to be discarded.

139. Absorption Spectra.—When light from a source giving a continuous spectrum passes through a vapor or gas, there will be a strong selective absorption of certain wave lengths. These are found to coincide with some of the possible emission wave lengths. This is to be expected according to the idea of energy levels, because absorption corresponds to an increase in atomic energy and, therefore, to upward transitions. Not all the emission lines can become absorption lines when the atom is in the normal state. Only those lines which have the normal valence orbit as their common final orbit can be absorbed. An excited atom

[1] X-ray unit (X. U.) = 10^{-11} centimeter.

will absorb the lines for which the end orbit is the orbit of one of its excited electrons.

When light from an arc passes through sodium vapor and is analyzed spectroscopically, dark lines will replace the ordinary emission lines. Such dark lines are characteristic of the absorption by gases at ordinary and low pressures, or by some substances in very dilute solutions. At very high pressures and for liquids and solids, the absorption, if selective at all, consists of broad bands.

The dark Fraunhofer lines in the spectrum of sunlight are nearly all due to absorption by the atmosphere of the sun. Being

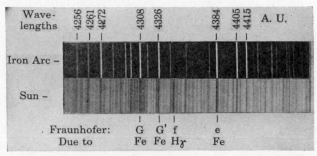

FIG. 141.—The *G* region of the solar spectrum compared with the spectrum of an iron arc.

at a very high temperature, the solar atmosphere contains vapors of even the elements we know commonly as solids. These exert a strongly selective absorption of the continuous radiation from the hot and relatively much denser interior. Many of these dark lines have been found to correspond in position to the emission lines of common terrestrial elements (Fig. 141). It is certain that at least forty of our elements exist on the sun.

In a similar way, the spectroscope can give information regarding the constitution of other luminous celestial bodies, such as the stars, nebulae, and comets. The planets and the moon shine by reflected light, so that, except for the absorption by their atmosphere, the reflected light has the same constitution as sunlight. Other celestial bodies, however, are self-luminous, presumably because of their high temperature. Their spectra differ greatly, as is shown by the prominence of certain series of lines in some of them, but the whole mass of evidence shows that their constituent elements are the same as those of the earth and the sun.

From the intensities and presence of some of the lines, or from the wave length of the most intense continuous radiation, if present, the temperature of radiating celestial bodies can be estimated. It appears that the gaseous nebulae which give a bright line spectrum are the hottest, having temperatures around 20,000 to 30,000°C., according to Saha. The blue-white stars are cooler, while the reddish stars are still cooler. Stars at all kinds of temperatures are seen in the heavens; hence it is thought that these are all stages in the eternal cycle of evolution of suns. The gaseous nebula cools, contracts, and there are formed suns and

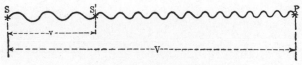

Fig. 142.—Doppler effect.

their planetary systems. In ages the suns cool and become dark but are again rekindled by a gigantic collision which forms another nebula and starts the process over again.

It is noticed that if the spectrum of a star is photographed alongside the spectrum of hydrogen, for example, the lines of hydrogen in the two pictures will not have quite the same wave lengths. All of the lines will be found displaced very slightly one way or the other. This effect is produced by stars either approaching or receding from the earth. Just as the pitch of sound is raised if the source is approaching the observer and lowered if the source is receding, so also in the case of light a corresponding effect is noticed for very high velocities. This is known as the Doppler effect, and it enables one to determine how fast the source is approaching or receding. If v is the velocity of the source toward the observer, V is the velocity of light, and λ is the wave length, then in one second the source, which was at S (Fig. 142), has moved to S' a distance v away. In this same time, the light emitted at the beginning of the second will be at P, a distance V from S. Since the source is oscillating with some definite frequency ν, there are ν waves emitted in each second.

Hence ν waves all lie between S' and P, so that the wave length of one is $\dfrac{V - v}{\nu}$. Calling this λ', we have

$$\lambda' = \frac{V - v}{\nu}.$$

For a stationary source

$$\nu = \frac{V}{\lambda},$$

so that on substituting we get

$$\lambda' = \left(1 - \frac{v}{V}\right)\lambda,$$

or

$$\lambda - \lambda' = \frac{v}{V}\lambda.$$

Now $V = 3 \times 10^{10}$ centimeters per second, so that the velocity v can be calculated if λ and $\lambda - \lambda'$ are measured spectroscopically.

The velocities of stars vary between 1 and 100 kilometers per second. This can be measured spectroscopically to within 1 kilometer per second. On the average, the stars on one side of the heavens are found to be approaching the solar system, and on the other side they are receding. This is taken to mean that the solar system is moving in the former direction.

140. Dispersion and Absorption.—It has been pointed out that most substances refract violet light through a greater angle than red. This is so commonly the case that when it was found that some materials refract red through a greater angle than violet, the dispersion was said to be *anomalous*. It was early shown that materials which possess anomalous dispersion for visible light are always strongly colored, and that their dispersion is normal when the wave lengths are not too near the absorption band. When it became possible to measure dispersion for wave lengths outside the visible range, it was found that all materials possess absorption bands in which their dispersion is anomalous. The term *selective dispersion* is better for this reason. The effect was at first thought to be unusual only because, customarily, materials transparent in the visible region are considered, and in all such cases the experimenter is not very close to any absorption band. Figure 143 shows the variation of the index of absorption κ and the index of refraction with changing wave length through an absorption band. Selective dispersion can be explained by the effect on the velocity of the light which is produced by a large number of oscillators having a definite resonance frequency.

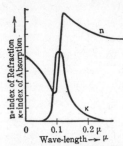

FIG. 143.—Selective dispersion and absorption.

When the frequency of the wave approaches the resonance frequency, the absorption of energy from the wave increases and the velocity of the wave is altered. The modified velocity can be calculated theoretically and from this the index of refraction can be obtained. The theoretical results agree well with the experimental.

141. Photochemistry.—Sometimes the absorption of radiant energy and the consequent excitation or ionization of atoms starts and promotes chemical reactions. The study of such reactions is called *photochemistry*. Light may cause either combination or dissociation of certain compounds, as illustrated by the following reversible reactions:

$$2H_2 + O_2 \rightleftarrows 2H_2O$$
$$2CO + O_2 \rightleftarrows 2CO_2$$
$$H_2 + Cl_2 \rightleftarrows 2HCl$$
$$H_2 + Br_2 \rightleftarrows 2HBr$$

The third reaction in this list takes place with explosive violence when a strong beam of light, *e.g.*, sunlight, falls on a mixture of chlorine and hydrogen in the right proportion. This and other reactions are produced by visible light, but usually the shorter wave lengths are more effective.

The action of light on a photographic plate is an example of photochemical reduction. The silver salts in the sensitive emulsion are converted by the light into a form suitable for complete reduction to silver by the chemicals of the developing solution. This reduced silver is finely divided and black.

The greatest photographic action is caused by violet or ultraviolet waves and the least by the yellow and red. The red rays have such a slight effect that ordinary plates are made, handled, and developed in red light without damage. It is, however, possible to make plates sensitive to red and yellow by the use of dyes such as pinacynol, dicyanin, or neocyanin. Plates sensitive as far as the yellow, but not the red, are called *orthochromatic*, while those sensitive even for the red are called *panchromatic*. These plates must be handled in total darkness and developed by a timing method. It is interesting that the addition of an absorbing dye for the red will make the plate much more sensitive to that color.

The use of dyes for a similar purpose is found in nature in the leaves of plants. The growth of plants depends on a photochemical process. Sunlight is absorbed by the green chlorophyll, which makes possible, among other things, the combination of carbon dioxide and water to form starch and other organic compounds. This is a most important chemical reaction, for all life on this earth depends on it. Only plants are able to convert inorganic compounds into living tissue. All other forms of life require food of organic nature, and this comes either from plants directly or from animals which eat plants.

142. Photoelectric Effects.—Normally, gases are very good insulators, but it is found that short waves have the power of making them slightly conducting. The increased conductivity is due to the removal of electrons from the atoms by the light. The resulting ions and electrons are the carriers of the current when an electric field is applied between some two electrodes in the gas.

In the study of this effect, Hallwachs found that when the electrodes were illuminated there was a greater current. He soon found that only the negative electrode need be illuminated to produce this effect and that no change in conductivity resulted if the light fell on the positive electrode. In fact, even if the electrodes are in a vacuum, which is a most perfect insulator, a current can be obtained if light of short enough wave length falls on the negative electrode. Now, the passage of an electric current in a vacuum can take place only by means of charged particles; hence there must be some of these emitted by the negative electrode when illuminated. These must have a negative charge, since they cannot leave the positive electrode when the light falls on it. It has since been shown that these particles are electrons because their charges and masses check with those of electrons produced by other means. The expulsion of electrons from metals by light is called *photoelectricity*. Each metal has a definite long-wave limit at which the effect starts, only waves shorter than this being effective. The photoelectric expulsion of electrons is usually studied in a high vacuum, so as to eliminate complications due to ionization of air, the currents measured being purely electronic.

The kinetic energy of the expelled electrons can be measured by means of the difference in potential that will just stop them. It is found that the energy, and, therefore, the velocity, of each electron is independent of the intensity of the light. Thus a stronger light emits merely more electrons, but with no greater velocity than if very weak light of the same frequency were used. The kinetic energies are, however, found proportional to the frequency of the light. The numerical value of the constant of proportionality is the same as Planck's constant h. If W is the energy, then it is found that

$$W = h\nu - p,$$

where p is a small correction equal to the amount of energy necessary to get the electron free of the surface of the substance after it has received a quantum of energy from the light. This is a sort of latent "heat" of evaporation of the electrons and determines the long-wave limit. It is called the "work function" of the substance. The equation above is often referred to as *Einstein's photoelectric equation*. Since the energy of an electron of charge e is equal to eV, where V is the potential difference necessary to stop it, the above is usually written as

$$eV = h\nu - p.$$

This equation has been carefully tested and the most accurate measurements of h have been obtained with its aid.

The photoelectric threshold, or long-wave limit, is found by putting V equal to zero and solving for the wave length. The result $\dfrac{hc}{p}$ depends on the material used.

At very high frequencies, the term $h\nu$ becomes so large that p can be neglected in comparison with it. This condition holds when X-rays or gamma rays are used, so that, in this case

$$h\nu = eV.$$

From this expression the formula for the wave length of the radiation can easily be obtained in terms of the voltage necessary to stop the photoelectrons. This was given early in this chapter as one method for measuring the wave lengths of such rays.

Photoelectric cells are sometimes used to measure the intensity of radiation. For any definite wave length, the number of electrons, and hence the current, is proportional to the intensity. The current is usually measured by an electrometer or a very sensitive galvanometer. A disadvantage of a photoelectric cell is that it is not equally sensitive to all wave lengths.

Sometimes selenium cells are used for measuring intensities. These operate on a somewhat different principle, since it is the resistance of the selenium itself, instead of the surrounding space, which is decreased by the light. This is called the "actino-electric effect" and is also a property of other materials besides selenium. There is no simple relation between current and intensity or between current and wave length. A selenium cell can be made very sensitive to light, especially if its resistance is high. It must be calibrated carefully, and then used under exactly the same conditions in order to give reliable results.

Further information on the methods of physical photometry is given in Art. 19.

Problems

1. A star having the same type of spectrum as the sun has its maximum emission for a wave length of 4,000 Å. U. What is the approximate temperature of the star? *Ans.* 7010°C.

2. The D_1 line of sodium, whose wave length is 5,890.2 Å. U., is found displaced in the spectrum of a star by 0.2 Å. U. toward the violet. What is the velocity of the star in the line of sight? Is it approaching or receding? *Ans.* 10.2 km. per sec.; approaching.

3. What are the wave lengths of the first lines in the Lyman, Balmer, and Paschen series of hydrogen, Rydberg's constant being 3.290×10^{15}? *Ans.* (a) 1,217 Å. U.; (b) 6,565 Å. U.; (c) 18,770 Å. U.

4. The shortest line in the K series of X-ray lines of molybdenum is 0.6193 Å. U. What is the minimum voltage which must be used to obtain the K series of molybdenum? *Ans.* 19,940 volts.

5. The photoelectric effect of a certain metal sets in at a wave length of 4,000 Å. U. How much energy is required to barely get the electron out of the metal? *Ans.* 4.91×10^{-12} erg.

6. How much energy will the electron have in the case of the above metal if light having a wave length of 3,000 Å. U. is used?   *Ans.* 1.64 × 10⁻¹² erg.

7. How many ergs in a quantum of (*a*) sodium light, and (*b*) in X-rays of 1 Å. U. wave length?   *Ans.* (*a*) 3.34 × 10⁻¹² erg; (*b*) 1.97 × 10⁻⁸ erg.

8. An electron falls through a difference in potential of 30,000 volts. What is its energy?   What is the shortest wave length that it can cause to be emitted?   *Ans.* (*a*) 4.77 × 10⁻⁸ erg; (*b*) 0.411 Å. U.

CHAPTER XIV

THE THEORY OF RELATIVITY

143. The Ether Theory.—Between the time of its emission at a source and its arrival at an observer, radiant energy exists and travels in some all-pervading medium which is called the *ether*. This medium must fill the entire universe, and the light from the stars may be imagined as coming through it in the form of electric waves. Its mechanical properties must be those of a perfectly non-viscous fluid in order that the heavenly bodies may move through it without hindrance. The earth moves through it much as a sphere would move through water, but with no friction whatever. From our position, the ether must be streaming past the earth with some velocity depending on the motion of the solar system and on the orbital motion and rotation of the earth. Now there is no way of finding the absolute velocity of the solar system, but it is known that the average orbital velocity of the earth is 30 kilometers per second. The velocity of the ether stream past the earth's surface must be at least this amount or, if it is less in one season, it must be correspondingly greater a half year later.

Michelson and Morley, two American physicists, devised an optical experiment capable of easily measuring the relative velocity of earth and ether. It consisted of a 16-foot interferometer of the type previously invented by Michelson and explained in Art. 102. By multiple reflections, the arms were made equivalent in length to 64 feet. Suppose that the ether stream is in the direction of one of the arms, as indicated in Fig. 144. They calculated that although the arms MA and MB are made exactly equal, it would take light longer to travel with and then against stream from M to A to M than it did across stream from M to B to M. Every swimmer knows that the analogous fact holds true for swimming in a river. In this case the light wave is the swimmer and the ether stream is the river. Assuming that light travels with a velocity c with respect to the ether, and that the velocity of the apparatus through the ether is v, they found that the path difference between the two interfering rays is approximately (*i.e.* if v/c is small)

$$R = L\frac{v^2}{c^2},$$

where L is the length of the interferometer. By turning the apparatus through 90 degrees, they interchanged the arms and

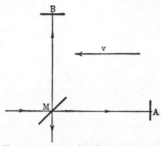

produced the opposite path difference. One-half of the total change in the path difference of the two rays as measured by the motion of the fringes should give the value of R.

Their experiment showed, however, that the above theory is wrong or that something has been omitted, for as far as they could tell, there was no perceptible effect, although the apparatus was delicate enough

Fig. 144.—Michelson-Morley experiment.

to detect the expected result. Hence they concluded it was impossible to measure the velocity of the ether stream, or, in other words, to measure the absolute velocity of the earth through space.

The explanation forwarded by Fitzgerald and by Lorentz almost simultaneously was that the apparatus must have contracted enough in the direction of the earth's motion through the ether, namely, by the amount $\frac{L}{2}\frac{v^2}{c^2}$, so that the times of traversal of both paths were equal. This idea is in accordance with the electron theory of matter, for the motion of a swarm of electrons would create magnetic forces tending to contract the body.

Besides the Michelson-Morley experiment, there have been other experiments designed for the purpose of measuring the velocity of the earth through the ether. All of these also have failed. As far as we know, the earth's motion does not affect any phenomenon or, if it does, something else covers up the effect. As far as can be ascertained, the velocity of the earth through the ether may be a half the velocity of light, in which case bodies would be contracted by about one-eighth of their length in the direction of motion. Contrary to the first impression, these changes would not be measurable or even perceptible, for everything would be affected in the same way. The measuring rods would shrink by the same amount as soon as placed alongside for comparison. Moreover, the effect could not be seen, because the retinas of our eyes would also be contracted in the same proportion in this direction, no matter how we turned our eyes. This is not so, however, if we are not moving with the rod; *i.e.*, a difference in length would be noticed in this case depending on our relative velocity. Thus we arrive at the important conclusion that we cannot decide the true length of a rod until we know how rapidly it moves through the ether. Since there is no way of finding this prerequisite, we shall never know the true length of anything.

144. Einstein's Theory of Relativity.—In 1905 Einstein published a very important paper on what he called the theory of relativity. He expressed the view that the contractions and other complications in moving systems are not real but due to a misinterpretation of Nature. Einstein's view is that nothing happens to the arms of the interferometer when they are rotated, but that the result indicates that the velocity of light is the same in all directions regardless of the velocity of the source or observer through the ether. This view would certainly be incorrect in the case of sound waves or water waves, for it is known that any motion of the transmitting medium past a measuring apparatus would change the observed velocity by exactly the velocity of the medium. In calculating the expected value of R, this same idea was applied to light waves and was disproved by the experiment, instead of being masked by a compensating contraction, says Einstein. That is to say, Einstein prefers to deny the contraction and to conclude rather that the velocity of light is the same for all observers under all conditions of motion. This interpretation of the Michelson-Morley experiment disposes of its negative result very simply, but it leads to quite revolutionary conclusions as to the metrical properties of space and time. In particular, it requires that the length of anything (*e.g.*, a rod) moving with a velocity v with respect to an observer is actually

less in the ratio of $\sqrt{1 - \dfrac{v^2}{c^2}}$:1 than if relatively at rest. Otherwise the velocity of light measured by the observer with this
rod would not be the same regardless of his velocity. Every
other observer moving with a different velocity would require a
different value for the length of the rod. This appears to be the
same conclusion as reached by Lorentz; in fact, the formula for the
relative lengths as measured by two different observers is exactly
the same; but there is a subtle difference between the theories of
Lorentz and Einstein. Imagine a large number of moving systems with their associated observers and assume that they move
with various velocities. If all these observers measure the
length of the same thing, both theories agree that the observed
values will not be the same, and they even agree as to the com-
parative values obtained. The difference is that Lorentz assumes
that one of these many observers obtains the true length because
he is at rest in the ether, while the others disagree because of their
contracted measuring rods. Although he admits we can never
know which observer is more "fundamental" in this respect than
the others, the point is that the assumption is made that such a
one exists. Einstein, on the other hand, proposes that all
observers are right and that they all get the true length of the
object. He is less partial than Lorentz. The fact that they
obtain different values he takes to mean that length is not an
absolute property of the object but depends on both the object
and the observer. Thus a rod actually has any number of
lengths all at once, one for each observer. Hence, the distance
between any two points on the earth or in the universe is not an
absolute thing. This is the meaning of the *relativity* of space.

Besides arriving at this conclusion, Einstein also finds that
measurements of time depend on the observer's velocity. Since
the Michelson-Morley experiment shows that the velocity of
light is the same, regardless of the motion of the source or the
observer, we can measure time by means of the distance a light
wave travels. The distances are best measured across the
direction of motion to avoid contractions, real or apparent.
Thus let A (Fig. 145) be an observer on a "stationary" system
and let him measure the time for light to travel from A to the
mirror M and back to A. Let PM be a similar distance across the

direction of motion on a system moving with a velocity v with
respect to the first.   Let these distances be compared and both
found equal to L.   Both observers obtain the same value for the
velocity of light on their systems and on each other's in accordance with Einstein's interpretation of the Michelson-Morley
experiment.   Suppose A's viewpoint is taken for the present.

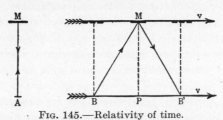

Fig. 145.—Relativity of time.

The paths of the light in his and B's measurements of the velocity
are, respectively, AMA and BMB'.   Their relative values are
found to be

$$(AM)^2 = (PM)^2 = (BM)^2 - (BP)^2,$$

so that

$$\frac{(AM^2)}{(BM^2)} = 1 - \frac{v^2}{c^2}.$$

Thus the paths are in the ratio of $\sqrt{1 - \frac{v^2}{c^2}} : 1$.   Therefore, if
B is to get the same velocity of light as A, his units of time must
be larger than A's in the same ratio; *i.e.*, his clocks must run
slower than A's.   Now, the most remarkable thing about this is
that B has the same right to claim that he is at rest and his light
beam goes straight over and back, while A's takes the longer
path.   The case is similar to that of a rubber ball thrown against
the wall of a railway coach by a man inside.   The ball appears to
travel straight across, to the man inside, but to take a diagonal
course to an observer outside.   In our case, however, the equal
right to the claim of being at rest is more apparent.   Since the
Michelson-Morley experiment tells us that their measurements of
c must give the same result, we must conclude that the units of
time are different for measurements on a system traveling
relatively to us.   Hence, A will contend B's clocks are slow, while

B will maintain that *A*'s are slow. If each measures the time interval between the same two occurrences, their results will not agree. Now neither of them is really more fundamental than the other, so there is no criterion for a proper choice between their results. Einstein states that they both obtain the right value, and that time, like space, is not absolute but depends on the observer. It is interesting that, although time and space are individually not absolute, a four-dimensional combination of the two is absolute. "Distances" in this space-time are the same for all observers, but an adequate discussion of the significance of this would take too much space and abstract mathematics.

Now when physical quantities are measured, lengths and times, or quantities derived from them, are always measured. With modern measuring apparatus this is not always apparent, but it is nevertheless true when the construction and calibration of the instruments are considered. Therefore, practically all measurements are relative, the result depending as much on the motion of the observer as on the magnitude of what he is measuring. Practically, however, as long as we measure things which are at rest relatively to ourselves, or are moving with velocities not having the order of magnitude of the velocity of light, the effects described above are negligible. Most observations fall in this category, so that the practical aspect of relativity is negligible. The conclusions are, however, of great importance philosophically and they find application in astronomy, in observations on the motions of the high-speed particles emitted by radioactive materials, and in theories of atomic structure and radiation.

145. The Generalized Theory of Relativity.—Einstein later generalized his theory to include gravitational phenomena. Starting out from the above, which is called the *restricted theory* of relativity, he found that although lengths and times change with relative motion, many of the mathematical expressions of physical laws preserve their form. He assumed that all absolutely correct expressions of the laws of physics must be invariant under this so-called velocity transformation. This is much more general than simply assuming that the velocity of light is invariant. It means that if a mathematical expression does not preserve its original algebraic form when the lengths and times which appear in it are replaced by the modified quantities at any velocity, it cannot serve as a law of nature. It may still, however, hold very exactly for low velocities; yet it will be found wrong at higher velocities and so it cannot be a complete expression of the true law.

For this and other reasons, the Newtonian law of gravity did not fit in well with the theory of relativity. To bring the two into harmony Einstein proposed an entirely new theory of gravitation. He observed that an acceleration of a system was equivalent to the introduction of a gravitational attraction. An aviator banking around a curve is pushed down in his seat as if gravitation had increased and changed in direction. In looping the loop he is accelerated toward the center of curvature of his path so rapidly that it may be that he is forced to his seat even when upside down. The equivalence of the two kinds of force is still more marked when it is called to mind that no device except a gyroscope has been invented that will tell the aviator which way is "down" at all times. The gyroscope does not depend on gravitation but must, in the beginning, be set in the direction wanted, and it will then continually indicate that direction. Instruments depending on the force of gravitation are always affected in the same way by an acceleration. Hence, Einstein concludes that gravitation is equivalent to an acceleration.

Einstein then postulates that there is a distortion of space and time near matter, such that the gravitating body is really moving in a straight line with a uniform velocity in this crooked space. To us it appears to be accelerated because of the artificial way in which we look at space and time. Because we think the body is accelerated, we say there must be a force acting. Einstein says there is no force, unless by holding the body we prevent it from following its natural course. If we let go of it, there will be no force acting on it, since it is really moving in a straight line with uniform velocity when the distortion of space and time are taken into consideration. A simple analogy is that of centrifugal force. If the earth, for example, revolved at a very high speed, things would tend to fly off. To us they would appear to be accelerated upward if we let go of them. If we were not aware of the true nature of the phenomenon, we would likely say that the earth repelled everything. Moreover, the upward acceleration would be the same for all bodies regardless of their mass, just as in the case of gravitation. Hence the force would be proportional to the mass. The force of gravitation is just this kind of force. Some day, it would be discovered that the earth really exerts no force of repulsion, but that if we look at the thing in a more fundamental way, all bodies tend to preserve their state of motion in a straight line with a uniform velocity (really flying off on a tangent) and that there is no force unless they are prevented from doing this. It is just this kind of theory of gravitation that Einstein proposes. He states that gravity is a fictitious geometrical force introduced because of apparent accelerations, which in turn arise from not considering the true nature of space and time which are distorted near matter. Now, the space that Einstein considers to be distorted near matter is, to the confusion of the non-mathematically minded, not our ordinary three-dimensional space, but the four-dimensional space of length and time. Moreover, this time is multiplied by the square root of minus one. Space of which these are four dimensions cannot be visualized, but it can be treated mathematically like three-dimensional space by merely introducing a fourth variable; and that is all it means. One of the chief advantages of mathematics is that every symbol in every equation does not have to be visualized. It is this four-dimensional space which is distorted into a purely mathematical fifth dimension near matter. It may be said that the distorted space is equivalent to matter, or that it is matter. In this space, bodies always tend to move in such a way that they follow the shortest path between two points. Unless we use this type of space, bodies will appear to be accelerated toward each other, and hence apparently attracted. The theory, as is evident, is purely mathematical. Equations in four variables are set up and the processes are applied by which the equation of the shortest possible path between two points is found, and the result is the equation of motion of a body in a gravitational field. This theory would, however, lead us to believe that it is of no use to look for causes of gravitation, that the real fact is a crookedness of space. Dr. W. F. G. Swann[1] tells an interesting story to illustrate this point.

[1] *Science*, Vol. 41, p. 457, 1925.

The gist of Dr. Swann's analogy is as follows:

Imagine a crater, in the middle of which is a house, and let there be an observer so high above it that he can see only the horizontal plan of things. Suppose he sees a man walk across the crater. The traveler will naturally take the shortest path, which is neither straight through the house, nor around the edge of the crater. The shortest path will lead him part way down, then around, and then up again. This is what we see and know to be true about the path he chooses. The distant observer, however, will only see that the man's path is not straight, being apparently deviated by the house. He will probably say that the house exerts a force on the man. After studying the form of the path, he may set up equations for the force and perhaps devise theories to explain why the force exists.

These theories may lead to the imagination of various complicated sorts of mechanisms, leading far from the fundamental cause, which, in this case, is the crookedness of the surface of the earth.

So, in the case of gravitation, Einstein concludes that the fundamental cause is the crookedness of space, and that it is a waste of energy to bother about the origin of the force of gravitation. He has investigated the nature of the curvature of space by a very intricate mathematical analysis. In this way he has been able to re-calculate the orbits of the planets and to solve other gravitational problems. He has in this way devised a law of gravitation which satisfies the requirements of relativity and reduces to Newton's law when the velocity is small. His conclusions explain some peculiar motions of the planet Mercury which Newton's theory left unsolved. It also predicts a slight bending, or gravitation, of a beam of light when it passes massive bodies such as the sun. Astronomical observations of the apparent positions of stars, when their light passes near the sun, can be made only during total eclipses. The effect is small and difficult to measure accurately. What measurements have been obtained so far are, on the whole, in good agreement with the result predicted by Einstein. New observations are being made at every eclipse. Another effect predicted is a slight shift in the wave length of all spectrum lines toward the red when the source is near a very large mass such as the sun. This is due to the distortion of the time dimension of the four-dimensional space near matter. The effect is also very small and must be distinguished from the Doppler effect. The value found agrees with that predicted. These three effects have never been satisfactorily explained before by any theory. Einstein's theory not only explains them but gives the correct numerical values.

CHAPTER XV

THE NATURE OF LIGHT

146. The Corpuscular Properties of Light.—There are still many unsolved problems in connection with the nature of light, as well as of electricity and matter. Under these circumstances there is some doubt as to whether an entrance into this subject should not be barred except to those workmen engaged in the building up of the theory. In spite of this misgiving, and the knowledge that this chapter will necessarily leave the problem in an unsatisfactory state, some of the salient features of the ultimate theory will be pointed out, for even now these can be seen, although it is impossible to be certain of the manner in which they will be eventually joined together.

It was realized as early as 1905 by Einstein that the quantum phenomena, *e.g.*, the photoelectric effect, suggest that light is corpuscular. As has been shown (Art. 142), the energy of a photoelectron does not depend on the intensity of the light. Only the number of liberated electrons varies with the intensity of the light. This contradicts the wave theory, for a high intensity in this case means a high amplitude, and this should eject the electrons more violently. On a corpuscular point of view, however, the result is perfectly clear, for in this case a high light intensity means a greater number of light corpuscles, or *photons* as they are now called, and these should liberate a proportionately greater number of electrons. The fact that the energy of each photoelectron is proportional to the frequency of the light indicates that the energy W of each photon is proportional to the frequency ν in accordance with the quantum relation:

$$W = h\nu. \tag{a}$$

One can use this equation to translate the corpuscularly undesirable term "frequency" into photon energy. According to Einstein's theory of relativity, energy, W, has a mass, m, of amount W/c^2, where c is the velocity of light. Hence each photon would have a momentum, M, equal to mc, or W/c. Consequently

$$M = \frac{h\nu}{c} = \frac{h}{\lambda}. \tag{b}$$

These two equations, (a) and (b), describe the mechanical properties of a photon.[1]

This theory was not immediately accepted; even Einstein himself was doubtful of its truth and regarded it at first only as a tool which is very effective in dealing with problems on the interaction between matter and radiation. There were, of course, many attempts to reconcile the wave theory with photoelectric and similar phenomena. To account for the dependence of the energy of the photoelectrons on the frequency and not on the intensity, it was assumed that the electron obtained its energy from the atom and not from the light, the light merely acting on a "trigger" to release the electrons. The electrons of greater energy could be associated with triggers which required higher frequencies. The electrons were like apples in a tree, a vigorous shaking would only free more electrons, but the energy would depend only on the level from which they came, and this could well be different for different frequencies. Another suggestion was that if the electrons received their energy from the light, there might be continuous absorption during which the energy would be stored up somehow by each electron until it amounted to a quantum. In this case only the *emission* of light and photoelectrons would be governed by quantum laws. However, all such attempts to reconcile waves with quantum phenomena have been generally given up in the face of the mounting evidence in favor of the photon theory as applied to these effects.

147. The Compton Effect.—The most beautiful confirmation of the reality of Einstein's light-quanta or photons is found in the Compton effect discovered in 1922 and named after the discoverer. X-rays of frequency ν are scattered by a block of some material, preferably of low atomic number for greater intensity, and it is found that the frequency of the scattered radiation ν' differs

---

[1] Since an atom may lose angular momentum during radiation, conservation of angular momentum requires that the photon may also have a spin.

from that of the incident radiation and that this difference is proportional to $\sin^2 \frac{\theta}{2}$, where θ is the angle of scattering. To explain this experiment, Compton assumes that the X-rays are scattered by the electrons in the scattering block. Then using Einstein's equations for the energy and momentum of each X-ray photon, he considers the results of an impact of a photon with an electron, using the principles of conservation of energy and momentum. The energy of the photon after impact, $h\nu'$, is less than that of the incident photon because of the energy imparted to the electron. This depends on the directness of the hit, which will also determine the angle of scattering. The result obtained by Compton expressed as a change in wave length is

$$\lambda' - \lambda = 2\frac{h}{mc} \sin^2 \frac{\theta}{2},$$

where m is the mass of the electron, and the other quantities have their usual significance. There are no unknown constants in this formula, so that the expected shift can easily be calculated and compared with the experimental results. The agreement is perfect. Naturally this is a strong argument for the photon theory. The wave theory explains the effect only qualitatively as a sort of Doppler effect, but it is powerless to give a quantitative agreement with experiment—at least without introducing arbitrary and contradictory ideas.

148. Interference Experiments.—In order not to lose sight of the power of the wave theory in its own domain, let us consider some interference experiments. Michelson's interferometer provides a number of difficulties for the photon theory. What happens when a photon strikes the half-silvered mirror of the interferometer (Art. 102)? Splitting it in two would change the color (energy) of the light particle. The photon must be either transmitted as a whole or reflected as a whole. What determines whether any particular photon should be reflected or transmitted? This uncertainty was first realized by Newton in dealing with a similar case of division of a beam of light at a refracting surface. To account for his observations in this kind of experiment, Newton postulated that the light particles underwent "fits of easy transmission and fits of easy reflection." The modern statement of this alternative behavior is termed the "uncertainty principle," which is a vital part of the new quantum mechanics. Thus it assumed that some quanta are transmitted and that others are reflected. But the interference bands themselves cause the next difficulty, for if the transmitted and reflected photons are independent particles, how can the destination of a particle traveling in one arm of a Michelson interferometer be influenced by the distance a different particle has to travel in the other arm? There must be this influence in order to give the interference bands which are observed.

There is, however, more than just interference to be explained; it must also be shown why there should be no interference if the difference in path is made greater than that required for coherence (Art. 98). A purely corpuscular theory is powerless to give satisfactory answers to these questions which are so directly explained by the wave theory.

A simpler experiment which leads to the same conclusion is Young's experiment. This experiment has been performed with light so weak that only a few quanta passed through the first slit in each second. Under these conditions the quanta must pass individually through one or the other of the two adjacent slits (Art. 28). Now, interference effects are not observed when light passes through only one slit and, here, although both slits are open, the light passes through only one hole or another if the photon theory is true. A long photographic exposure shows, however, that the interference pattern is actually of exactly the same character as in strong light. This shows either that the wave theory is true or that the original photon theory must be modified to at least include a "ghost" wave which guides the photons so that they will tend to arrive at the places of greatest amplitude.

The situation is then that of two conflicting theories, each of which is invincible in its own particular field. In connection with the transference of energy and momentum between radiation and matter, light behaves as though it were corpuscular. On the other hand, interference and diffraction effects show just as surely that light must have wavelike characteristics. Here is a dilemma, the way out of which has been suggested by another dilemma of similar character.

149. Electron Waves and Matter Waves.—We ordinarily think of electricity and matter as atomic—with nothing wavelike about them. However, in everyday experience light does not show its wave nature either. Interference and diffraction were discovered relatively late in the course of man's experimentation with light. The reason for this is that the wave length is so short that it requires circumstances which differ from everyday situations in order to make interference and diffraction noticeable. In the case of X-rays, interference effects were actually looked for by experienced investigators with modern facilities for many years before they were finally observed. Will a stream of electrons, or even atoms, show interference or diffraction effects under suitable conditions? In recent years this question has been answered in the affirmative. Electron diffraction was discovered by Davisson and Germer in 1927 when they were studying the reflection of electrons by a crystal of nickel. Instead of the ordinary type of reflection they found that the crystal formed a velocity spectrum of the electrons by reflecting different velocities in definite directions. Some time later it was found that atoms of hydrogen and helium also gave diffraction effects when reflected off a crystal of lithium fluoride. In these experiments, Bragg's equation (page 185) is found to hold with the wave length represented by the quantity

$$\lambda = \frac{h}{mv},$$

where m represents the mass, and v the velocity of the electron or atom. These experiments have now been repeated in many laboratories with many types of crystals and there is now no doubt that *electrons and atoms have wavelike properties* and that experiments such as Young's are theoretically workable although difficult actually to carry out. This is because the wave length is so extraordinarily short.

For ordinary particles the mass is so large in comparison with h that for any appreciable velocity, the DeBroglie wave length (as this associated wave length is called) is so short that diffraction effects are not observable. Thus the paths or trajectories of the particles are perfectly definite and we have no contradiction with ordinary mechanics. This is like geometrical optics, in that interference and diffraction effects are not considered and one may use the corpuscular theory with apparently complete success. It is only for very light particles not traveling at too great speeds, that the wavelike characteristics show themselves in diffraction phenomena. Only electrons and the lighter atoms have thus far been diffracted, but the implication is that all atoms, molecules, and even bodies of some size have wavelike characteristics, but the wave length is usually so short that diffraction effects are too small to be observed.

150. Wave Mechanics.—If all material bodies have wave like properties and obey the laws of interference and diffraction, then the fundamental mechanics must be a mechanics of waves, just as the fundamental optics has been long realized to be an optics of waves. However, geometrical optics is not discarded because of this but is used confidently when it is known that diffraction effects will not appreciably modify the result. This is now the place in physics of classical mechanics. It is even more generally applicable than geometrical optics, for the DeBroglie waves are so short that mechanical diffraction effects are much rarer than optical diffraction effects. The initial development of the new branch of physics called *wave mechanics* or the mechanics of "microscopic systems" is the work of DeBroglie and Schroedinger. Its particular sphere of application lies in the mechanics of electrons and atoms. In this mechanics it is customary to talk of particles but to calculate their destinations by means of waves. In some forms of the theory, the particles are considered to be localized groups of waves called *wave packets*. Such packets have the disadvantage that they cannot travel far without spreading.

In general, the particles are assumed to be the primary reality and the waves to be purely mathematical "ghost" waves. These waves have the significance that the square of their amplitude gives ·the probability for finding the particle at that particular point in space. When the number of particles is large, the square of the amplitude gives the density of the particles or, in the case of light, the intensity of the light.

In the special case of light, these waves are electromagnetic waves. That this must be true is a consequence of the family relationship of light to all the other electromagnetic radiations (see Art. 127 on the complete spectrum). It is not hard to ascribe corpuscularity to visible light or to radiation of shorter wave length, particularly if the corpuscles are governed by the laws of wave mechanics. However, it is difficult to think of anything but waves in regard to the very longest of the electro-magnetic waves. Nevertheless, these are of the same physical nature as visible light, differing only in wave length.

151. Action at a Distance.—In the case of light, one can avoid the dilemma between particles and waves by throwing the light theory overboard and adopting the viewpoint of action at a distance. This action can be described by perfectly specific laws in the form of mathematical equations, without the need of assuming anything really to pass over the intervening space between the source and the observer. The revival of this old idea is an outgrowth of the recent tendency to eliminate unob-servables from physical theory. Light is observed only in connection with material bodies and never in free space. Hence why assume that light exists at all in free space divorced from material bodies? The experimental fact is that energy and momentum disappear at one atom, to reappear at some later time at another atom. However, action at a distance requires vital changes in some physical laws. The principles of energy and momentum are violated first at the emitting atom. Later the energy and momentum (light pressure) reappear at another atom at a time which is equal to the distance between the atoms divided by the velocity of light. This reappearance of the energy and momentum is *by itself* as mysterious as the original dis-appearance, for it also violates the principles of conservation of energy and momentum. If, however, the radiating and receiving atoms are very close together, the two violations follow so closely after one another that for all practical purposes there is no contradiction with classical principles. But astronomers tell us that there are extra-galactic systems which are so far away that it takes light one hundred million years to reach the earth. When light reaches us from one of these bodies, we have the response to some atomic disturbance which took place before the human race, or perhaps any life whatever, appeared on this planet. It is hard to imagine the contemporary re-creation of this disturbance out of nothing. At this time and place the violation of the energy and momentum principles seems as real as it could possibly be. However, this does not deter the bolder of the physicists to uphold this theory and to modify the conservation principles to include the required time lag.

To the philosophically minded, this theory will surely not appeal very strongly, for these will wish to know how energy and momentum are transmitted from the source to the observer. Why do they follow a quite definite path through prisms, lenses, and by reflection off mirrors? The light can be blocked at any point along this path. It is very true that one does not need answers to these questions in order to calculate the results of light transmission, for equations are now known which will give the final results accurately. One prominent physicist said of the situation, "Long ago, we thought that we understood natural phenomena, but we could not calculate very much; now we can calculate a great deal, but we understand very little." This situation is not at all satisfying to one who likes to think of the physical causes and principles which underlie natural phenomena. However, the history of physics as well as experience with students shows that invariably mathematical formulas are mastered before their significance is realized. This is probably the situation in theoretical physics today, for the wave-mechanical methods for calculating atomic phenomena are still very new.

APPENDIX

UNITS OF LENGTH, METRIC SYSTEM

1 kilometer (km.)	= 1,000 meters (m.)
1 decimeter (dm.)	= 10^{-1} m.
1 centimeter (cm.)	= 10^{-2} m.
1 millimeter (mm.)	= 10^{-3} m.
1 micron (μ)	= 10^{-6} m.
1 millimicron (mμ)	= 10^{-9} m.
1 Ångström unit (Å. U.)	= 10^{-10} m.
1 X-ray unit (X. U.)	= 10^{-13} m.

CONVERSION ENGLISH TO METRIC

1 mile (mi.) = 1.6094 km.	1 foot (ft.) = 30.48 cm.
1 yard (yd.) = 0.9144 m.	1 inch (in.) = 2.5400 cm.

UNITS OF ENERGY

Centimeter-gram-second (c.g.s.) system

1 joule = 10^7 ergs
1 calorie = 4.181 joules

POWER

1 watt = 1 joule per second

ELECTRICAL UNITS

Conversion of practical units to c.g.s. electrostatic units (e.s.u.), and to c.g.s. electromagnetic units (e.m.u.)

1 volt = $\frac{1}{300}$ e.s.u. of difference in potential
1 volt = 10^8 e.m.u. of difference in potential
1 coulomb = 3×10^9 e.s.u. of quantity of electricity
1 coulomb = 10^{-1} e.m.u. of quantity of electricity

TABLE II.—REFLECTION

a. MIRRORS

Wave length in μ	Steel, per cent	Speculum (mirror bronze), per cent	Silver, per cent	Platinum, per cent	Glass mirrors	
					Ag-back, per cent	Hg-back, per cent
0.25	38	30	34	33		
0.35	49	51	68	43		
0.45	52	56	90	55	86	73
0.55	55	64	93	61	88	71
0.70	58	67	95	69	90	73
1.00	63	71	97	73		
4.00	88	89	98	91		
14.00	96	94	99	96		

b. DIFFUSE REFLECTION OF WHITE LIGHT

	Diffuse-light incidence, per cent	Normal incidence, per cent
Magnesium oxide.....................	96	92
Magnesium carbonate................	98	93
Plaster of Paris......................	91	87
Matt white celluloid.................	80 to 85	75 to 80
White blotting paper.................	80 to 85	75 to 80

TABLE III.—RADIANT EFFICIENCIES

The radiant efficiency of a source is the ratio of the energy radiated between wave lengths of 4,000 and 7,600 Ångström Units to the total radiant energy

Source	Radiant efficiency, per cent	"Black body" at, degrees absolute	Radiant efficiency, per cent
Candle.....................	0.96	1,000	0.0+
Welsbach mantle............	2.0	1,500	0.0+
Carbon-filament lamp........	2.5	2,000	1.7
Tungsten-filament lamp......	4.4	3,000	14.6
Sunlight...................	35	4,000	31.8
Arc (according to carbons)....	8 to 17	6,000	49.7 (max)
Mercury arc...............	41 to 48	8,000	47.7
		12,000	18.6

TABLE IV.—VISIBILITY FACTOR

Mechanical equivalent of light: 0.0015 watt per lumen* at 5,550 Ångström Units

Wave length in μ's	Visibility factor	Watts per lumen*	Wave length in μ's	Visibility factor	Watts per lumen*
0.40	0.0004	3.75	0.58	0.870	0.00172
0.42	0.0040	0.375	0.60	0.631	0.00238
0.44	0.023	0.0652	0.62	0.381	0.00396
0.46	0.060	0.0250	0.64	0.175	0.00857
0.48	0.139	0.0108	0.66	0.061	0.0241
0.50	0.323	0.00465	0.68	0.017	0.0872
0.52	0.710	0.00218	0.70	0.0041	0.366
0.54	0.954	0.00157	0.72	0.00105	1.43
0.56	0.995	0.00151	0.74	0.00025	6.00

* The lumen is the unit of light flux. One lumen is equal to the rate of flow of light energy passing normally through a unit area at a unit distance from a standard candle.

TABLE V.—MISCELLANEOUS RADIATION DATA

The "solar constant" is 1.932 calories per square centimeter per minute. Of this amount, 30 per cent is absorbed by the atmosphere when the sun is directly overhead; and 46 per cent is absorbed when the sun is 60 degrees from the zenith. This energy is divided among three principal regions of the spectrum about as follows:

Zenith sun (Washington)

Wave lengths	Calories per square centimeter per minute
0 to 0.45μ	0.13
0.45 to 0.70	0.53
0.70 to ∞	0.69

For value of some common illuminations, see page 16.
For value of the radiation constants of a "black body," see page 190.

Electroluminescence:

$$\lambda = 12,345./V$$
$$\nu = 8,100.V$$

where

λ is wave length in Ångström Units,
ν is wave number,
V is electron accelerating potential in volts.

For table of electromagnetic radiations and their wave length, see page 188.

TABLE VI.—WAVE LENGTHS OF PROMINENT LINES IN SOME SPECTRA*

Source	Wave length, Ångström units†	Source	Wave length, Ångström units†
Hydrogen arc.....	6,562.8	Sodium flame....	5,889.96
	4,861.3		5,895.93
	4,340.5	Mercury arc.....	6,234.4
Helium arc.......	7,065.2		5,790.3
	6,678.1		5,769.4
	5,875.6		5,460.8
	5,015.7		4,916.2
	4,921.0		4,358.4
	4,713.2		4,077.9
	4,471.5		4,046.6
Cadmium arc.....	6,438.4696	Barium cored	6,496.9
	(standard)	carbon arc.	6,141.9
	5,085.88		5,853.7
	4,799.91		5,535.5
	4,678.19		4,934.1
Lithium flame....	6,708.2		4,554.2

* For wave lengths of prominent Fraunhofer lines, see p. 56.
† International Ångström units. The wave lengths given are the values in air at 15°C. and 76 centimeters barometric pressure.

Table VII.—Indices of Refraction of Glass

Wave length (in Ångström Units)	Ordinary crown	Medium flint
4,046.6	1.53189	1.65788
4,077.9	1.53147	1.65692
4,340.5	1.52818	1.64973
4,358.4	1.52798	1.64931
4,861.3	1.52326	1.63941
4,916.2	1.52283	1.63854
5,460.8	1.51929	1.63143
5,769.4	1.51771	1.62834
5,790.3	1.51760	1.62815
5,893.0	1.51714	1.62725
6,234.4	1.51573	1.62458
6,562.8	1.51458	1.62241
6,708.2	1.51412	1.62157
7,682.0	1.51160	1.61701

Per cent composition
(Raw materials used)

Ingredient	Crown	Flint
SiO_2	67.0	45.6
Na_2O	12.0	3.4
K_2O	5.0	4.1
B_2O_3	3.5	....
BaO	10.6	....
ZnO	1.5	....
As_2O_3	0.4	....
CaO	....	3.0
PbO	....	44.0

Indices of other non-crystalline media, p. 49
Indices and dispersive powers, p. 57
Indices of uniaxial crystals, p. 155
Indices of biaxial crystals, p. 155

TABLE VIII.—CONSTANTS OF ATOMIC PHYSICS

Electronic charge, $e = 4.77 \times 10^{-10}$ e.s.u. $= 1.591 \times 10^{-20}$ e.m.u.

Gas constant, $R = 8.313 \times 10^7$ ergs per degree centigrade.

Loschmidt's number, $L = 6.062 \times 10^{23}$ atoms per gram atomic weight.

Mass of atom, $M = 1.65 \times 10^{-24}$ g. per unit atomic weight.

Mass of electron, $m_0 = 8.93 \times 10^{-28}$ g.

Number molecules, $N = 2.705 \times 10^{19}$ mol. per cubic centimeter at 0°C. and 76 centimeters barometric pressure.

Planck's constant, $h = 6.548 \times 10^{-27}$ erg-sec.

Rydberg's constant, $R = 3.290 \times 10^{15}$ vibrations per second.

Rydberg's constant, $R = 109677.7$ vibrations per centimeter.

Velocity of light, $c = 2.9986 \times 10^{10}$ cm. per second *in vacuo*.

TABLE IX.—ATOMIC WEIGHTS OF THE ELEMENTS

Symbol	Atomic number	Name	Atomic weight*	Symbol	Atomic number	Name	Atomic weight*
A	18	Argon	39.91	N	7	Nitrogen	14.008
Ac	89	Actinium	?	Na	11	Sodium	22.997
Ag	47	Silver	107.880	Nb	41	Niobium	See Cb
Al	13	Aluminum	26.96	Nd	60	Neodymium	144.27
As	33	Arsenic	74.96	Ne	10	Neon	20.2
Au	79	Gold	197.2	Ni	28	Nickel	58.69
				Nt	86	Niton	See Em
B	5	Boron	10.82				
Ba	56	Barium	137.37	O	8	Oxygen	16.000
Be	4	Beryllium	9.02	Os	76	Osmium	190.8
Bi	83	Bismuth	209.00				
Br	35	Bromine	79.916	P	15	Phosphorus	31.024
				Pa	91	Protoactinium	?
C	6	Carbon	12.000	Pb	82	Lead	207.20
Ca	20	Calcium	40.07	Pd	46	Palladium	106.7
Cb	41	Columbium	93.1	Po	84	Polonium	210
Cd	48	Cadmium	112.41	Pr	59	Praseodymium	140.92
Ce	58	Cerium	140.25	Pt	78	Platinum	195.23
Cl	17	Chlorine	35.458				
Co	27	Cobalt	58.97	Ra	88	Radium	225.95
Cp	71	Cassiopeium	175.0	Rb	37	Rubidium	85.44
Cr	24	Chromium	52.01	Re	75	Rhenium	?
Cs	55	Cesium	132.81	Rh	45	Rhodium	102.91
Ct	72	Celtium	?	Rn	86	Radon	See Em
Cu	29	Copper	63.57	Ru	44	Ruthenium	101.7
Dy	66	Dysprosium	162.52	S	16	Sulphur	32.065
				Sa	62	Samarium	150.43
Em	86	Ra-emanation	222	Sb	51	Antimony	121.77
Er	68	Erbium	167.7	Sc	21	Scandium	45.10
Eu	63	Europium	152.0	Se	34	Selenium	79.2
				Si	14	Silicon	28.06
F	9	Fluorine	19.00	Sm	62	Samarium	See Sa
Fe	26	Iron	55.84	Sn	50	Tin	118.70
				Sr	38	Strontium	87.62
Ga	31	Gallium	69.72				
Gd	64	Gadolinium	157.26	Ta	73	Tantalum	181.5
Ge	32	Germanium	72.38	Tb	65	Terbium	159.2
Gl	4	Glucinium	See Be	Te	52	Tellurium	127.5
				Th	90	Thorium	232.15
H	1	Hydrogen	1.0077	Ti	22	Titanium	47.9
He	2	Helium	4.00	Tl	81	Thallium	204.4
Hf	72	Hafnium	178.6	Tu	69	Thullium	169.4
Hg	80	Mercury	200.61				
Ho	67	Holmium	163.4	U	92	Uranium	238.17
				UX_2	91	Uranium-X_2	234
I	53	Iodine	126.932				
Il	61	Illinium	?	V	22	Vanadium	50.96
In	49	Indium	114.8				
Ir	77	Iridium	193.1	W	74	Tungsten	184.0
K	19	Potassium	39.095	Xe	54	Xenon	130.2
Kr	36	Krypton	82.9				
				Yb	70	Ytterbium	173.6
La	57	Lanthanum	138.91	Yt	39	Yttrium	89.0
Li	3	Lithium	6.939	Zn	30	Zinc	65.38
Lu	71	Lutecium	See Cp	Zr	40	Zirconium	91
Ma	43	Masurium	?				
Mg	12	Magnesium	24.32				
Mn	25	Manganese	54.93				
Mo	42	Molybdenum	96.0				

* International Critical Tables (1926).

TABLE X.—GROUPING OF ELECTRONS AROUND THE NUCLEUS ACCORDING TO BOHR (latest revision)

Columns give the number of electrons in the various groups or "shells"

Shell number*		1	2	2	3	3	3	4	4	4	4	5	5	5	6	6	6	7
Subdivision†			1	2	1	2	3	1	2	3	4	1	2	3	1	2	3	1
Atomic number	Element																	
1	H	1																
2	He	2																
3	Li	2	1															
4	Be	2	2															
5	B	2	2	1														
6	C	2	2	2														
7	N	2	2	3														
8	O	2	2	4														
9	F	2	2	5														
10	Ne	2	2	6														
11	Na	2	2	6	1													
12	Mg	2	2	6	2													
13	Al	2	2	6	2	1												
14	Si	2	2	6	2	2												
15	P	2	2	6	2	3												
16	S	2	2	6	2	4												
17	Cl	2	2	6	2	5												
18	A	2	2	6	2	6												
19	K	2	2	6	2	6	...	1										
20	Ca	2	2	6	2	6	...	2										
21	Sc	2	2	6	2	6	1	2										
22	Ti	2	2	6	2	6	2	2										
29	Cu	2	2	6	2	6	10	1										
30	Zn	2	2	6	2	6	10	2										
31	Ga	2	2	6	2	6	10	2	1									
32	Ge	2	2	6	2	6	10	2	2									
33	As	2	2	6	2	6	10	2	3									
34	Se	2	2	6	2	6	10	2	4									
35	Br	2	2	6	2	6	10	2	5									
36	Kr	2	2	6	2	6	10	2	6									
37	Rb	2	2	6	2	6	10	2	6	...	...	1						
38	Sr	2	2	6	2	6	10	2	6	...	...	2						
39	Y	2	2	6	2	6	10	2	6	1	...	2						
40	Zr	2	2	6	2	6	10	2	6	2	...	2						
47	Ag	2	2	6	2	6	10	2	6	10	...	1						
48	Cd	2	2	6	2	6	10	2	6	10	...	2						
49	In	2	2	6	2	6	10	2	6	10	...	2	1					
50	Sn	2	2	6	2	6	10	2	6	10	...	2	2					
51	Sb	2	2	6	2	6	10	2	6	10	...	2	3					
52	Te	2	2	6	2	6	10	2	6	10	...	2	4					
53	I	2	2	6	2	6	10	2	6	10	...	2	5					
54	X	2	2	6	2	6	10	2	6	10	...	2	6					
55	Cs	2	2	6	2	6	10	2	6	10	...	2	6	...	1			
56	Ba	2	2	6	2	6	10	2	6	10	...	2	6	...	2			
57	La	2	2	6	2	6	10	2	6	10	...	2	6	1	2			
58	Ce	2	2	6	2	6	10	2	6	10	1	2	6	1	2			
59	Pr	2	2	6	2	6	10	2	6	10	2	2	6	1	2			
71	Cp	2	2	6	2	6	10	2	6	10	13	2	6	1	2			
72	Hf	2	2	6	2	6	10	2	6	10	14	2	6	2	2			
79	Au	2	2	6	2	6	10	2	6	10	14	2	6	10	1			
80	Hg	2	2	6	2	6	10	2	6	10	14	2	6	10	2			
81	Tl	2	2	6	2	6	10	2	6	10	14	2	6	10	2	1		
86	Em	2	2	6	2	6	10	2	6	10	14	2	6	10	2	6		
87	......	2	2	6	2	6	10	2	6	10	14	2	6	10	2	6	...	1
88	Ra	2	2	6	2	6	10	2	6	10	14	2	6	10	2	6	...	2
89	Ac	2	2	6	2	6	10	2	6	10	14	2	6	10	2	6	1	2
90	Th	2	2	6	2	6	10	2	6	10	14	2	6	10	2	6	2	2
91																		
92	U																	

* Often called the "principal quantum number." (The first group forms the K "shell"; the second forms the L shell, etc.)
† Often called the "azimuthal quantum number."

TABLE XI.—SOME WAVE LENGTHS IN THE X-RAY SERIES OF THE MORE COMMON TARGET MATERIALS (Å.U.)

Element and atomic number	K series		L series		M series	
	Strong α_1 line	Shortest wave length	Strong α_1 line	Shortest wave length	Strong α_1 line	Shortest wave length
26 Fe...........	1.9321	1.7408	17.58	15.61		
29 Cu..........	1.5374	1.3782	13.306	12.10		
42 Mo..........	0.7078	0.6197	5.395	4.370		
45 Rh..........	0.6120	0.5340	4.588	3.677		
46 Pd...........	0.5843	0.5092	4.359	3.481		
74 W...........	0.2086	0.1790	1.474	1.026	6.969	5.163
78 Pt...........	0.1822	0.1589	1.310	0.895	6.034	4.451

Table XII.—Lowest Radiation Potentials and Ionization Potentials
of the Elements

Element	Lowest radiation potential, volts		Wave length, Ångström units corresponding to lowest radiation potential	Ionization potential, volts	
	Calculated	Observed		Calculated	Observed
A.............	11.57	11.5	1,066.8	15.7	15.2
Ag............	3.65	3.1	3,382.9	7.54	6.0(?)
Al............	3.13	....	3,944	5.96	
As............	4.44	4.7	2,780	....	11.5
Au............	4.61	....	2,676.1	9.20	
B.............	4.94	....	2,497	8.0	
Ba............	1.56	....	7,911	5.19	
Bi............	4.02	3.9	3,068	....	8.0
C.............	....	....	....	11.3	
Ca............	1.89	1.9	6,573	6.09	6.01
Cd............	3.78	3.95	3,271	8.95	8.92
Cl............	....	....	....	13.0	
Cr............	2.89	....	4,290	6.74	
Cs............	1.38	1.48	8,943.6	3.88	3.9
Cu............	3.77	....	3,274.1	7.69	7.8
F.............	....	....	....	16.9	
Ga............	3.06	....	4,033	5.97	
H.............	10.15	10.2	1,215.7	13.54	13.5
He............	20.55	20.55	600.5	24.48	24.5
Hg............	4.87	4.9	2,537	10.39	10.38
In............	3.01	....	4,102	5.76	
K.............	1.60	1.55	7,699.0	4.32	4.1
Kr............	9.99	9.9	1,235.8	....	12.5
Li............	1.84	....	6,708	5.37	
Mo............	3.16	....	3,903	7.35	
Mg............	2.70	2.65	4,571	7.61	7.75
N.............	....	....	....	14.5	
Na............	2.09	2.12	5,895.9	5.12	5.13
Ne............	....	....	....	21.4	
O.............	9.11	....	1,356	13.56	
P.............	....	....	....	13.3	
Pb............	4.35	....	2,833	7.39	7.93
Rb............	1.55	1.6	7,947.6	4.16	4.1
S.............	6.50	.....	1,900	10.31	
Sb............	5.34	5.6	2,311	....	9.0(?)
Se............	....	3.2(?)	....	....	12.7
Si............	....	....	....	10.3	
Sr............	1.79	....	6,893	5.67	
Te............	....	2.6(?)			
Tl............	3.27	....	3,776	6.08	6.04
X.............	8.40	8.3	1,469.5	....	10.9
Zn............	4.01	4.18	3,076	9.35	9.3

TABLE XIII.—RECIPROCALS

	0	1	2	3	4	5	6	7	8	9
10	0.01 0000	9901	9804	9709	9615	9524	9434	9346	9259	9174
11	0.00 9091	9009	8929	8850	8772	8696	8621	8547	8475	8403
12	0.00 8333	8264	8197	8130	8065	8000	7937	7874	7813	7752
13	0.00 7692	7634	7576	7519	7463	7407	7353	7299	7246	7194
14	0.00 7143	7092	7042	6993	6944	6897	6849	6803	6757	6711
15	0.00 6667	6623	6579	6536	6494	6452	6410	6369	6329	6289
16	0.00 6250	6211	6173	6135	6098	6061	6024	5988	5952	5917
17	0.00 5882	5848	5814	5780	5747	5714	5682	5650	5618	5587
18	0.00 5556	5525	5495	5464	5435	5405	5376	5348	5319	5291
19	0.00 5263	5236	5208	5181	5155	5128	5102	5076	5051	5025
20	0.00 5000	4975	4950	4926	4902	4878	4854	4831	4808	4785
21	0.00 4762	4739	4717	4695	4673	4651	4630	4608	4587	4566
22	0.00 4545	4525	4505	4484	4464	4444	4425	4405	4386	4367
23	0.00 4348	4329	4310	4292	4274	4255	4237	4219	4202	4184
24	0.00 4167	4149	4132	4115	4098	4082	4065	4049	4032	4016
25	0.00 4000	3984	3968	3953	3937	3922	3906	3891	3876	3861
26	0.00 3846	3831	3817	3802	3788	3774	3759	3745	3731	3717
27	0.00 3704	3690	3676	3663	3650	3636	3623	3610	3597	3584
28	0.00 3571	3559	3546	3534	3521	3509	3497	3484	3472	3460
29	0.00 3448	3436	3425	3413	3401	3390	3378	3367	3356	3344
30	0.00 3333	3322	3311	3300	3289	3279	3268	3257	3247	3236
31	0.00 3226	3215	3205	3195	3185	3175	3165	3155	3145	3135
32	0.00 3125	3115	3106	3096	3086	3077	3067	3058	3049	3040
33	0.00 3030	3021	3012	3003	2994	2985	2976	2967	2959	2950
34	0.00 2941	2933	2924	2915	2907	2899	2890	2882	2874	2865
35	0.00 2857	2849	2841	2833	2825	2817	2809	2801	2793	2786
36	0.00 2778	2770	2762	2755	2747	2740	2732	2725	2717	2710
37	0.00 2703	2695	2688	2681	2674	2667	2660	2653	2646	2639
38	0.00 2632	2625	2618	2611	2604	2597	2591	2584	2577	2571
39	0.00 2564	2558	2551	2545	2538	2532	2525	2519	2513	2506
40	0.00 2500	2494	2488	2481	2475	2469	2463	2457	2451	2445
41	0.00 2439	2433	2427	2421	2415	2410	2404	2398	2392	2387
42	0.00 2381	2375	2370	2364	2358	2353	2347	2342	2336	2331
43	0.00 2326	2320	2315	2309	2304	2299	2294	2288	2283	2278
44	0.00 2273	2268	2262	2257	2252	2247	2242	2237	2232	2227
45	0.00 2222	2217	2212	2208	2203	2198	2193	2188	2183	2179
46	0.00 2174	2169	2165	2160	2155	2151	2146	2141	2137	2132
47	0.00 2128	2123	2119	2114	2110	2105	2101	2096	2092	2088
48	0.00 2083	2079	2075	2070	2066	2062	2058	2053	2049	2045
49	0.00 2041	2037	2033	2028	2024	2020	2016	2012	2008	2004
50	0.00 2000	1996	1992	1988	1984	1980	1976	1972	1969	1965
51	0.00 1961	1957	1953	1949	1946	1942	1938	1934	1931	1927
52	0.00 1923	1919	1916	1912	1908	1905	1901	1898	1894	1890
53	0.00 1887	1883	1880	1876	1873	1869	1866	1862	1859	1855
54	0.00 1852	1848	1845	1842	1838	1835	1832	1828	1825	1821

TABLE XIII.—RECIPROCALS (*Continued*)

	0	1	2	3	4	5	6	7	8	9
55	0.00 1818	1815	1812	1808	1805	1802	1799	1795	1792	1789
56	0.00 1786	1783	1779	1776	1773	1770	1767	1764	1761	1757
57	0.00 1754	1751	1748	1745	1742	1739	1736	1733	1730	1727
58	0.00 1724	1721	1718	1715	1712	1709	1706	1704	1701	1698
59	0.00 1695	1692	1689	1686	1684	1681	1678	1675	1672	1669
60	0.00 1667	1664	1661	1658	1656	1653	1650	1647	1645	1642
61	0.00 1639	1637	1634	1631	1629	1626	1623	1621	1618	1616
62	0.00 1613	1610	1608	1605	1603	1600	1597	1595	1592	1590
63	0.00 1587	1585	1582	1580	1577	1575	1572	1570	1567	1565
64	0.00 1563	1560	1558	1555	1553	1550	1548	1546	1543	1541
65	0.00 1538	1536	1534	1531	1529	1527	1524	1522	1520	1517
66	0.00 1515	1513	1511	1508	1506	1504	1502	1499	1497	1495
67	0.00 1493	1490	1488	1486	1484	1481	1479	1477	1475	1473
68	0.00 1471	1468	1466	1464	1462	1460	1458	1456	1453	1451
69	0.00 1449	1447	1445	1443	1441	1439	1437	1435	1433	1431
70	0.00 1429	1427	1425	1422	1420	1418	1416	1414	1412	1410
71	0.00 1408	1406	1404	1403	1401	1399	1397	1395	1393	1391
72	0.00 1389	1387	1385	1383	1381	1379	1377	1376	1374	1372
73	0.00 1370	1368	1366	1364	1362	1361	1359	1357	1355	1353
74	0.00 1351	1350	1348	1346	1344	1342	1340	1339	1337	1335
75	0.00 1333	1332	1330	1328	1326	1325	1323	1321	1319	1318
76	0.00 1316	1314	1312	1311	1309	1307	1305	1304	1302	1300
77	0.00 1299	1297	1295	1294	1292	1290	1289	1287	1285	1284
78	0.00 1282	1280	1279	1277	1276	1274	1272	1271	1269	1267
79	0.00 1266	1264	1263	1261	1259	1258	1256	1255	1253	1252
80	0.00 1250	1248	1247	1245	1244	1242	1241	1239	1238	1236
81	0.00 1235	1233	1232	1230	1229	1227	1225	1224	1222	1221
82	0.00 1220	1218	1217	1215	1214	1212	1211	1209	1208	1206
83	0.00 1205	1203	1202	1200	1199	1198	1196	1195	1193	1192
84	0.00 1190	1189	1188	1186	1185	1183	1182	1181	1179	1178
85	0.00 1176	1175	1174	1172	1171	1170	1168	1167	1166	1164
86	0.00 1163	1161	1160	1159	1157	1156	1155	1153	1152	1151
87	0.00 1149	1148	1147	1145	1144	1143	1142	1140	1139	1138
88	0.00 1136	1135	1134	1133	1131	1130	1129	1127	1126	1125
89	0.00 1124	1122	1121	1120	1119	1117	1116	1115	1114	1112
90	0.00 1111	1110	1109	1107	1106	1105	1104	1103	1101	1100
91	0.00 1099	1098	1096	1095	1094	1093	1092	1091	1089	1088
92	0.00 1087	1086	1085	1083	1082	1081	1080	1079	1078	1076
93	0.00 1075	1074	1073	1072	1071	1070	1068	1067	1066	1065
94	0.00 1064	1063	1062	1060	1059	1058	1057	1056	1055	1054
95	0.00 1053	1052	1050	1049	1048	1047	1046	1045	1044	1043
96	0.00 1042	1041	1040	1038	1037	1036	1035	1034	1033	1032
97	0.00 1031	1030	1029	1028	1027	1026	1025	1024	1022	1021
98	0.00 1020	1019	1018	1017	1016	1015	1014	1013	1012	1011
99	0.00 1010	1009	1008	1007	1006	1005	1004	1003	1002	1001

TABLE XIV.—TRIGONOMETRIC FUNCTIONS (0 to 10°)

Degrees	Sin	Cos	Tan	Cot
0° 00′	0.0000	1.0000	0.0000	∞
10	.0029	1.0000	.0029	343.77
20	.0058	1.0000	.0058	171.89
30	.0087	1.0000	.0087	114.59
40	.0116	0.9999	.0116	85.940
50	.0145	.9999	.0145	68.750
1° 00′	0.0175	0.9998	0.0175	57.290
10	.0204	.9998	.0204	49.104
20	.0233	.9997	.0233	42.964
30	.0262	.9997	.0262	38.188
40	.0291	.9996	.0291	34.368
50	.0320	.9995	.0320	31.242
2° 00′	0.0349	0.9994	0.0349	28.636
10	.0378	.9993	.0378	26.432
20	.0407	.9992	.0407	24.542
30	.0436	.9990	.0437	22.904
40	.0465	.9989	.0466	21.470
50	.0494	.9988	.0495	20.206
3° 00′	0.0523	0.9986	0.0524	19.081
10	.0552	.9985	.0553	18.075
20	.0581	.9983	.0582	17.169
30	.0610	.9981	.0612	16.350
40	.0640	.9980	.0641	15.605
50	.0669	.9978	.0670	14.924
4° 00′	0.0698	0.9976	0.0699	14.301
10	.0727	.9974	.0729	13.727
20	.0756	.9971	.0758	13.197
30	.0785	.9969	.0787	12.706
40	.0814	.9967	.0816	12.251
50	.0843	.9964	.0846	11.826
5° 00′	0.0872	0.9962	0.0875	11.430
10	.0901	.9959	.0904	11.059
20	.0929	.9957	.0934	10.712
30	.0958	.9954	.0963	10.385
40	.0987	.9951	.0992	10.078
50	.1016	.9948	.1022	9.7882
6° 00′	0.1045	0.9945	0.1051	9.5144
10	.1074	.9942	.1080	9.2553
20	.1103	.9939	.1110	9.0098
30	.1132	.9936	.1139	8.7769
40	.1161	.9932	.1169	8.5555
50	.1190	.9929	.1198	8.3450
7° 00′	0.1219	0.9925	0.1228	8.1443
10	.1248	.9922	.1257	7.9530
20	.1276	.9918	.1287	7.7704
30	.1305	.9914	.1317	7.5958
40	.1334	.9911	.1346	7.4287
50	.1363	.9907	.1376	7.2687
8° 00′	0.1392	0.9903	0.1405	7.1154
10	.1421	.9899	.1435	6.9682
20	.1449	.9894	.1465	6.8269
30	.1478	.9890	.1495	6.6912
40	.1507	.9886	.1524	6.5606
50	.1536	.9881	.1554	6.4348
9° 00′	0.1564	0.9877	0.1584	6.3138
10	.1593	.9872	.1614	6.1970
20	.1622	.9868	.1644	6.0844
30	.1650	.9863	.1673	5.9758
40	.1679	.9858	.1703	5.8708
50	.1708	.9853	.1733	5.7694
10° 00′	0.1736	0.9848	0.1763	5.6713

TABLE XV.—TRIGONOMETRIC FUNCTIONS

Arc.	Angle.	Sin.	Tan.	Sec.	Cosec.	Cot.	Cos.		
0.0000	0	0.0000	0.0000	1.0000	∞	∞	1.0000	90	1.5708
0.0175	1	0.0175	0.0175	1.0002	57.2987	57.2900	0.9998	89	1.5533
0.0349	2	0.0349	0.0349	1.0006	28.6537	28.6363	0.9994	88	1.5359
0.0524	3	0.0523	0.0524	1.0014	19.1073	19.0811	0.9986	87	1.5184
0.0698	4	0.0698	0.0699	1.0024	14.3356	14.3007	0.9976	86	1.5010
0.0873	5	0.0872	0.0875	1.0038	11.4737	11.4301	0.9962	85	1.4835
0.1047	6	0.1045	0.1051	1.0055	9.5668	9.5144	0.9945	84	1.4661
0.1222	7	0.1219	0.1228	1.0075	8.2055	8.1443	0.9925	83	1.4486
0.1396	8	0.1392	0.1405	1.0098	7.1853	7.1154	0.9903	82	1.4312
0.1571	9	0.1564	0.1584	1.0125	6.3925	6.3138	0.9877	81	1.4137
0.1745	10	0.1736	0.1763	1.0154	5.7588	5.6713	0.9848	80	1.3963
0.1920	11	0.1908	0.1944	1.0187	5.2408	5.1446	0.9816	79	1.3788
0.2094	12	0.2079	0.2126	1.0223	4.8097	4.7046	0.9781	78	1.3614
0.2269	13	0.2250	0.2309	1.0263	4.4454	4.3315	0.9744	77	1.3439
0.2443	14	0.2419	0.2493	1.0306	4.1336	4.0108	0.9703	76	1.3264
0.2618	15	0.2588	0.2679	1.0353	3.8637	3.7321	0.9659	75	1.3090
0.2793	16	0.2756	0.2867	1.0403	3.6280	3.4874	0.9613	74	1.2915
0.2967	17	0.2924	0.3057	1.0457	3.4203	3.2709	0.9563	73	1.2741
0.3142	18	0.3090	0.3249	1.0515	3.2361	3.0777	0.9511	72	1.2566
0.3316	19	0.3256	0.3443	1.0576	3.0716	2.9042	0.9455	71	1.2392
0.3491	20	0.3420	0.3640	1.0642	2.9238	2.7475	0.9397	70	1.2217
0.3665	21	0.3584	0.3839	1.0711	2.7904	2.6051	0.9336	69	1.2043
0.3840	22	0.3746	0.4040	1.0785	2.6695	2.4751	0.9272	68	1.1868
0.4014	23	0.3907	0.4245	1.0864	2.5593	2.3559	0.9205	67	1.1694
0.4189	24	0.4067	0.4452	1.0946	2.4586	2.2460	0.9135	66	1.1519
0.4363	25	0.4226	0.4663	1.1034	2.3662	2.1445	0.9063	65	1.1345
0.4538	26	0.4384	0.4877	1.1126	2.2812	2.0503	0.8988	64	1.1170
0.4712	27	0.4540	0.5095	1.1223	2.2027	1.9626	0.8910	63	1.0996
0.4887	28	0.4695	0.5317	1.1326	2.1301	1.8807	0.8829	62	1.0821
0.5061	29	0.4848	0.5543	1.1434	2.0627	1.8040	0.8746	61	1.0647
0.5236	30	0.5000	0.5774	1.1547	2.0000	1.7321	0.8660	60	1.0472
0.5411	31	0.5150	0.6009	1.1666	1.9416	1.6643	0.8572	59	1.0297
0.5585	32	0.5299	0.6249	1.1792	1.8871	1.6003	0.8480	58	1.0123
0.5760	33	0.5446	0.6494	1.1924	1.8361	1.5399	0.8387	57	0.9948
0.5934	34	0.5592	0.6745	1.2062	1.7883	1.4826	0.8290	56	0.9774
0.6109	35	0.5736	0.7002	1.2208	1.7434	1.4281	0.8192	55	0.9599
0.6283	36	0.5878	0.7265	1.2361	1.7013	1.3764	0.8090	54	0.9425
0.6458	37	0.6018	0.7536	1.2521	1.6616	1.3270	0.7986	53	0.9250
0.6632	38	0.6157	0.7813	1.2690	1.6243	1.2799	0.7880	52	0.9076
0.6807	39	0.6293	0.8098	1.2868	1.5890	1.2349	0.7771	51	0.8901
0.6981	40	0.6428	0.8391	1.3054	1.5557	1.1918	0.7660	50	0.8727
0.7156	41	0.6561	0.8693	1.3250	1.5243	1.1504	0.7547	49	0.8552
0.7330	42	0.6691	0.9004	1.3456	1.4945	1.1106	0.7431	48	0.8378
0.7505	43	0.6820	0.9325	1.3673	1.4663	1.0724	0.7314	47	0.8203
0.7679	44	0.6947	0.9657	1.3902	1.4396	1.0355	0.7193	46	0.8029
0.7854	45	0.7071	1.0000	1.4142	1.4142	1.0000	0.7071	45	0.7854
		Cos.	Cot.	Cosec.	Sec.	Tan.	Sin.	Angle.	Arc.

TABLE XVI.—LOGARITHMS OF TRIGONOMETRIC FUNCTIONS

Angle.	Log Sin.	Log Tan.	Log Sec.	Log Csc.	Log Cot.	Log Cos.	
0	$-\infty$	$-\infty$	0.0000	∞	∞	0.0000	90
1	8.2419	8.2419	0.0001	1.7581	1.7581	9.9999	89
2	8.5428	8.5431	0.0003	1.4572	1.4569	9.9997	88
3	8.7188	8.7194	0.0006	1.2812	1.2806	9.9994	87
4	8.8436	8.8446	0.0011	1.1564	1.1554	9.9989	86
5	8.9403	8.9420	0.0017	1.0597	1.0580	9.9983	85
6	9.0192	9.0216	0.0024	0.9808	0.9784	9.9976	84
7	9.0859	9.0891	0.0032	0.9141	0.9109	9.9968	83
8	9.1436	9.1478	0.0042	0.8564	0.8522	9.9958	82
9	9.1943	9.1997	0.0054	0.8057	0.8003	9.9946	81
10	9.2397	9.2463	0.0066	0.7603	0.7537	9.9934	80
11	9.2806	9.2887	0.0081	0.7194	0.7113	9.9919	79
12	9.3179	9.3275	0.0096	0.6821	0.6725	9.9904	78
13	9.3521	9.3634	0.0113	0.6479	0.6366	9.9887	77
14	9.3837	9.3968	0.0131	0.6163	0.6032	9.9869	76
15	9.4130	9.4281	0.0151	0.5870	0.5719	9.9849	75
16	9.4403	9.4575	0.0172	0.5597	0.5425	9.9828	74
17	9.4659	9.4853	0.0194	0.5341	0.5147	9.9806	73
18	9.4900	9.5118	0.0218	0.5100	0.4882	9.9782	72
19	9.5126	9.5370	0.0243	0.4874	0.4630	9.9757	71
20	9.5341	9.5611	0.0270	0.4659	0.4389	9.9730	70
21	9.5543	9.5842	0.0298	0.4457	0.4158	9.9702	69
22	9.5736	9.6064	0.0328	0.4264	0.3936	9.9672	68
23	9.5919	9.6279	0.0360	0.4081	0.3721	9.9640	67
24	9.6093	9.6486	0.0393	0.3907	0.3514	9.9607	66
25	9.6259	9.6687	0.0427	0.3741	0.3313	9.9573	65
26	9.6418	9.6882	0.0463	0.3582	0.3118	9.9537	64
27	9.6570	9.7072	0.0501	0.3430	0.2928	9.9499	63
28	9.6716	9.7257	0.0541	0.3284	0.2743	9.9459	62
29	9.6856	9.7438	0.0582	0.3144	0.2562	9.9418	61
30	9.6990	9.7614	0.0625	0.3010	0.2386	9.9375	60
31	9.7118	9.7788	0.0669	0.2882	0.2212	9.9331	59
32	9.7242	9.7958	0.0716	0.2758	0.2042	9.9284	58
33	9.7361	9.8125	0.0764	0.2639	0.1875	9.9236	57
34	9.7476	9.8290	0.0814	0.2524	0.1710	9.9186	56
35	9.7586	9.8452	0.0866	0.2414	0.1548	9.9134	55
36	9.7692	9.8613	0.0920	0.2308	0.1387	9.9080	54
37	9.7795	9.8771	0.0977	0.2205	0.1229	9.9023	53
38	9.7893	9.8928	0.1035	0.2107	0.1072	9.8965	52
39	9.7989	9.9084	0.1095	0.2011	0.0916	9.8905	51
40	9.8081	9.9238	0.1157	0.1919	0.0762	9.8843	50
41	9.8169	9.9392	0.1222	0.1831	0.0608	9.8778	49
42	9.8255	9.9544	0.1289	0.1745	0.0456	9.8711	48
43	9.8338	9.9697	0.1359	0.1662	0.0303	9.8641	47
44	9.8418	9.9848	0.1431	0.1582	0.0152	9.8569	46
45	9.8495	0.0000	0.1505	0.1505	0.0000	9.8495	45
	Log Cos.	Log Cot.	Log Csc.	Log Sec.	Log Tan.	Log Sin.	Angle.

(From Zeleny and Erikson's "Manual of Physical Measurements.")

TABLE XVII.—LOGARITHMS OF NUMBERS FROM 1 TO 1,000

	0	1	2	3	4	5	6	7	8	9	1 2 3	4 5 6	7 8 9
10	0000	0043	0086	0128	0170	0212	0253	0294	0334	0374	4 8 12	17 21 25	29 33 37
11	0414	0453	0492	0531	0569	0607	0645	0682	0719	0755	4 8 11	15 19 23	26 30 34
12	0792	0828	0864	0899	0934	0969	1004	1038	1072	1106	3 7 10	14 17 21	24 28 31
13	1139	1173	1206	1239	1271	1303	1335	1367	1399	1430	3 6 10	13 16 19	23 26 29
14	1461	1492	1523	1553	1584	1614	1644	1673	1703	1732	3 6 9	12 15 18	21 24 27
15	1761	1790	1818	1847	1875	1903	1931	1959	1987	2014	3 6 8	11 14 17	20 22 25
16	2041	2068	2095	2122	2148	2175	2201	2227	2253	2279	3 5 8	11 13 16	18 21 24
17	2304	2330	2355	2380	2405	2430	2455	2480	2504	2529	2 5 7	10 12 15	17 20 22
18	2553	2577	2601	2625	2648	2672	2695	2718	2742	2765	2 5 7	9 12 14	16 19 21
19	2788	2810	2833	2856	2878	2900	2923	2945	2967	2989	2 4 7	9 11 13	16 18 20
20	3010	3032	3054	3075	3096	3118	3139	3160	3181	3201	2 4 6	8 11 13	15 17 19
21	3222	3243	3263	3284	3304	3324	3345	3365	3385	3404	2 4 6	8 10 12	14 16 18
22	3424	3444	3464	3483	3502	3522	3541	3560	3579	3598	2 4 6	8 10 12	14 15 17
23	3617	3636	3655	3674	3692	3711	3729	3747	3766	3784	2 4 6	7 9 11	13 15 17
24	3802	3820	3838	3856	3874	3892	3909	3927	3945	3962	2 4 5	7 9 11	12 14 16
25	3979	3997	4014	4031	4048	4065	4082	4099	4116	4133	2 3 5	7 9 10	12 14 15
26	4150	4166	4183	4200	4216	4232	4249	4265	4281	4298	2 3 5	7 8 10	11 13 15
27	4314	4330	4346	4362	4378	4393	4409	4425	4440	4456	2 3 5	6 8 9	11 13 14
28	4472	4487	4502	4518	4533	4548	4564	4579	4594	4609	2 3 5	6 8 9	11 12 14
29	4624	4639	4654	4669	4683	4698	4713	4728	4742	4757	1 3 4	6 7 9	10 12 13
30	4771	4786	4800	4814	4829	4843	4857	4871	4886	4900	1 3 4	6 7 9	10 11 13
31	4914	4928	4942	4955	4969	4983	4997	5011	5024	5038	1 3 4	6 7 8	10 11 12
32	5051	5065	5079	5092	5105	5119	5132	5145	5159	5172	1 3 4	5 7 8	9 11 12
33	5185	5198	5211	5224	5237	5250	5263	5276	5289	5302	1 3 4	5 6 8	9 10 12
34	5315	5328	5340	5353	5366	5378	5391	5403	5416	5428	1 3 4	5 6 8	9 10 11
35	5441	5453	5465	5478	5490	5502	5514	5527	5539	5551	1 2 4	5 6 7	9 10 11
36	5563	5575	5587	5599	5611	5623	5635	5647	5658	5670	1 2 4	5 6 7	8 10 11
37	5682	5694	5705	5717	5729	5740	5752	5763	5775	5786	1 2 3	5 6 7	8 9 10
38	5798	5809	5821	5832	5843	5855	5866	5877	5888	5899	1 2 3	5 6 7	8 9 10
39	5911	5922	5933	5944	5955	5966	5977	5988	5999	6010	1 2 3	4 5 7	8 9 10
40	6021	6031	6042	6053	6064	6075	6085	6096	6107	6117	1 2 3	4 5 6	8 9 10
41	6128	6138	6149	6160	6170	6180	6191	6201	6212	6222	1 2 3	4 5 6	7 8 9
42	6232	6243	6253	6263	6274	6284	6294	6304	6314	6325	1 2 3	4 5 6	7 8 9
43	6335	6345	6355	6365	6375	6385	6395	6405	6415	0425	1 2 3	4 5 6	7 8 9
44	6435	6444	6454	6464	6474	6484	6493	6503	6513	6522	1 2 3	4 5 6	7 8 9
45	6532	6542	6551	6561	6571	6580	6590	6599	6609	6618	1 2 3	4 5 6	7 8 9
46	6628	6637	6646	6656	6665	6675	6684	6693	6702	6712	1 2 3	4 5 6	6 7 8
47	6721	6730	6739	6749	6758	6767	6776	6785	6794	6803	1 2 3	4 5 5	6 7 8
48	6812	6821	6830	6839	6848	6857	6866	6875	6884	6893	1 2 3	4 4 5	6 7 8
49	6902	6911	6920	6928	6937	6946	6955	6964	6972	6981	1 2 3	4 4 5	6 7 8
50	6990	6998	7007	7016	7024	7033	7042	7050	7059	7067	1 2 3	3 4 5	6 7 8
51	7076	7084	7093	7101	7110	7118	7126	7135	7143	7152	1 2 3	3 4 5	6 7 8
52	7160	7168	7177	7185	7193	7202	7210	7218	7226	7235	1 2 2	3 4 5	6 7 7
53	7243	7251	7259	7267	7275	7284	7292	7300	7308	7316	1 2 2	3 4 5	6 6 7
54	7324	7332	7340	7348	7356	7364	7372	7380	7388	7396	1 2 2	3 4 5	6 6 7

TABLE XVII.—LOGARITHMS OF NUMBERS FROM 1 TO 1,000 (*Continued*)

	0	1	2	3	4	5	6	7	8	9	1 2 3	4 5 6	7 8 9
55	7404	7412	7419	7427	7435	7443	7451	7459	7466	7474	1 2 2	3 4 5	5 6 7
56	7482	7490	7497	7505	7513	7520	7528	7536	7543	7551	1 2 2	3 4 5	5 6 7
57	7559	7566	7574	7582	7589	7597	7604	7612	7619	7627	1 2 2	3 4 5	5 6 7
58	7634	7642	7649	7657	7664	7672	7679	7686	7694	7701	1 1 2	3 4 4	5 6 7
59	7709	7716	7723	7731	7738	7745	7752	7760	7767	7774	1 1 2	3 4 4	5 6 7
60	7782	7789	7796	7803	7810	7818	7825	7832	7839	7846	1 1 2	3 4 4	5 6 6
61	7853	7860	7868	7875	7882	7889	7896	7903	7910	7917	1 1 2	3 4 4	5 6 6
62	7924	7931	7938	7945	7952	7959	7966	7973	7980	7987	1 1 2	3 3 4	5 6 6
63	7993	8000	8007	8014	8021	8028	8035	8041	8048	8055	1 1 2	3 3 4	5 5 6
64	8062	8069	8075	8082	8089	8096	8102	8109	8116	8122	1 1 2	3 3 4	5 5 6
65	8129	8136	8142	8149	8156	8162	8169	8176	8182	8189	1 1 2	3 3 4	5 5 6
66	8195	8202	8209	8215	8222	8228	8235	8241	8248	8254	1 1 2	3 3 4	5 5 6
67	8261	8267	8274	8280	8287	8293	8299	8306	8312	8319	1 1 2	3 3 4	5 5 6
68	8325	8331	8338	8344	8351	8357	8363	8370	8376	8382	1 1 2	3 3 4	4 5 6
69	8388	8395	8401	8407	8414	8420	8426	8432	8439	8445	1 1 2	2 3 4	4 5 6
70	8451	8457	8463	8470	8476	8482	8488	8494	8500	8506	1 1 2	2 3 4	4 5 6
71	8513	8519	8525	8531	8537	8543	8549	8555	8561	8567	1 1 2	2 3 4	4 5 5
72	8573	8579	8585	8591	8597	8603	8609	8615	8621	8627	1 1 2	2 3 4	4 5 5
73	8633	8639	8645	8651	8657	8663	8669	8675	8681	8686	1 1 2	2 3 4	4 5 5
74	8692	8698	8704	8710	8716	8722	8727	8733	8739	8745	1 1 2	2 3 4	4 5 5
75	8751	8756	8762	8768	8774	8779	8785	8791	8797	8802	1 1 2	2 3 3	4 5 5
76	8808	8814	8820	8825	8831	8837	8842	8848	8854	8859	1 1 2	2 3 3	4 5 5
77	8865	8871	8876	8882	8887	8893	8899	8904	8910	8915	1 1 2	2 3 3	4 4 5
78	8921	8927	8932	8938	8943	8949	8954	8960	8965	8971	1 1 2	2 3 3	4 4 5
79	8976	8982	8987	8993	8998	9004	9009	9015	9020	9025	1 1 2	2 3 3	4 4 5
80	9031	9036	9042	9047	9053	9058	9063	9069	9074	9079	1 1 2	2 3 3	4 4 5
81	9085	9090	9096	9101	9106	9112	9117	9122	9128	9133	1 1 2	2 3 3	4 4 5
82	9138	9143	9149	9154	9159	9165	9170	9175	9180	9186	1 1 2	2 3 3	4 4 5
83	9191	9196	9201	9206	9212	9217	9222	9227	9232	9238	1 1 2	2 3 3	4 4 5
84	9243	9248	9253	9258	9263	9269	9274	9279	9284	9289	1 1 2	2 3 3	4 4 5
85	9294	9299	9304	9309	9315	9320	9325	9330	9335	9340	1 1 2	2 3 3	4 4 5
86	9345	9350	9355	9360	9365	9370	9375	9380	9385	9390	1 1 2	2 3 3	4 4 5
87	9395	9400	9405	9410	9415	9420	9425	9430	9435	9440	0 1 1	2 2 3	3 4 4
88	9445	9450	9455	9460	9465	9469	9474	9479	9484	9489	0 1 1	2 2 3	3 4 4
89	9494	9499	9504	9509	9513	9518	9523	9528	9533	9538	0 1 1	2 2 3	3 4 4
90	9542	9547	9552	9557	9562	9566	9571	9576	9581	9586	0 1 1	2 2 3	3 4 4
91	9590	9595	9600	9605	9609	9614	9619	9624	9628	9633	0 1 1	2 2 3	3 4 4
92	9638	9643	9647	9652	9657	9661	9666	9671	9675	9680	0 1 1	2 2 3	3 4 4
93	9685	9689	9694	9699	9703	9708	9713	9717	9722	9727	0 1 1	2 2 3	3 4 4
94	9731	9736	9741	9745	9750	9754	9759	9763	9768	9773	0 1 1	2 2 3	3 4 4
95	9777	9782	9786	9791	9795	9800	9805	9809	9814	9818	0 1 1	2 2 3	3 4 4
96	9823	9827	9832	9836	9841	9845	9850	9854	9859	9863	0 1 1	2 2 3	3 4 4
97	9868	9872	9877	9881	9886	9890	9894	9899	9903	9908	0 1 1	2 2 3	3 4 4
98	9912	9917	9921	9926	9930	9934	9939	9943	9948	9952	0 1 1	2 2 3	3 4 4
99	9956	9961	9965	9969	9974	9978	9983	9987	9991	9996	0 1 1	2 2 3	3 3 4

INDEX